The HORSE ANATOMY WORKBOOK

The HORSE ANATOMY WORKBOOK

A learning aid for students based on
Peter Goody's classic work, *Horse Anatomy*

Maggie Raynor

J. A. ALLEN

First published in Great Britain in 2006 by J. A. Allen, an imprint of
The Crowood Press, Ramsbury, Marlborough, Wiltshire, SN8 2HR

www.crowood.com

This impression 2019

British Library Cataloguing-in-Publication Data
A catalogue record for this book is available from the British Library

ISBN 978 0 85131 905 6

This study book for students is closely based on the text and diagrams of
Peter Goody's *Horse Anatomy* (J.A. Allen).

Design by Judy Linard
Line illustrations by the author
Edited by Martin Diggle

Printed and bound in India by Replika Press Pvt Ltd

Contents

How to use this book

The purpose of this book is to act as a study tool, to help you familiarize yourself with, and commit to memory, the horse's anatomy.

Each double page spread consists of two elements – the figure (a drawing, or set of drawings) and the accompanying text. In some of the skeletal drawings, bones are separated to provide additional views of joint surfaces, etc. The text consists of a list of features to be coloured or labelled on the drawing(s). Where the overall figure consists of more than one drawing, the text (and instructions) may be modified to take account of this. Some general points to bear in mind are:

- In some cases, different parts of an anatomical feature may be visible at more than one point on a drawing, in which case its number may appear more than once on that drawing.

- Where there are two or more drawings to an overall figure, these drawings will often contain *different views of the same structure*. In such cases, the instructions given will be common to all the relevant drawings, e.g. 'On all drawings on which they occur, identify and colour the following.'

- In other cases, a figure may consist of two (or more) drawings, with *different features individually numbered on each* – i.e. part I on fig.(a) will be a different structure from part I on fig.(b). Where this occurs, the colouring instructions on the text page will appear under the relevant sub-headings.

Some structures (for example, some ligaments) occur in pairs. In some views, both structures will be visible. However, to avoid over-cluttering the drawings, only one of the pair may be numbered and arrowed (for example, with some views of medial and lateral collateral ligaments, only one may be identified). In line with the convention in Goody's Horse Anatomy, *and for reasons of consistency, such structures are always referred to in the terms 'medial and lateral…'; whether the actual structure labelled is, in fact, medial or lateral, will depend on the orientation of the drawings.*

Colouring

Each structure to be coloured on the drawing is indicated within the text by a circled number. Locate the structure on the drawing and colour it, then use the same colour to fill in the circled number within the text. You may also find it helpful to highlight or underline the text.

In some instances, where the nature or location of the structure to be identified is such that the structure itself cannot readily be coloured, the number identifying it is contained within a circle or a square. In these cases, colour the circle or square.

There are some drawings that contain a large number of structures to be coloured. If you are limited by the number of colours you have available, try to vary the colours used on adjacent structures.

Test the colours before using them – dark colours will obscure labelling and detail, so use only lighter shades.

Labelling

Structures to be labelled are indicated within the text by a bold capital letter. Locate the structure on the drawing and write in the appropriate labelling. You may also find it helpful to label any of the coloured structures that are particularly important, or difficult to remember.

Always read through the text before beginning to work on a drawing – occasionally procedures other than colouring or labelling are involved.

PART I – Overview

DIRECTIONAL TERMS (Figure 1)

Figures I(a) and (b) are concerned with directional terms which describe the location of various body structures. Figures I(c), (d) and (e) illustrate body planes (with the exception of the terms medial and lateral).

Fig. I(a) Lateral View I

Label:

A Dorsal (indicates the location of a structure towards the back)

B Ventral (indicates the location of a structure towards the belly)

C Cranial (describes the location of a body part towards the skull)

D Caudal (describes the location of a body part towards the tail)

E Rostral (specifically in the head, describes the location of a part towards the nose)

F Proximal (indicates a location towards the top of a limb)

G Distal (indicates a location towards the foot of a limb)

Fig. I(b) Lateral View 2

These terms are used when referring to the limbs.

Label:

A Cranial (a structure located to the front of a forelimb above the knee)

B Dorsal (a structure located to the front of a forelimb below the knee)

C Caudal (a structure located to the rear of a forelimb above the knee)

D Palmar (a structure located to the rear of a forelimb below the knee)

E Cranial (a structure located to the front of a hind limb above the hock)

F Dorsal (a structure located to the front of a hind limb below the hock)

G Caudal (a structure located to the rear of a hind limb above the hock)

H Plantar (a structure located to the rear of a hind limb below the hock)

Fig. I(c) Lateral View 3

Label:

A Dorsal, or frontal, planes (run through a body part parallel to its dorsal surface)

B Transverse planes (pass through any body part perpendicular to the part's long axis)

Fig. I(d) From Above

Label:

A Median plane (divides the head and trunk longitudinally into left and right halves)

B Sagittal planes (are parallel to the median plane)

Fig. I(e) Cranial View

Label:

A Median plane (definition as in Fig. I (d) A above)

B Medial (refers to structures located towards the median plane – in the limbs, refers to the inner side)

C Lateral (refers to structures located away from the median plane – in the limbs, refers to the outer side)

FIGURE 1: DIRECTIONAL TERMS

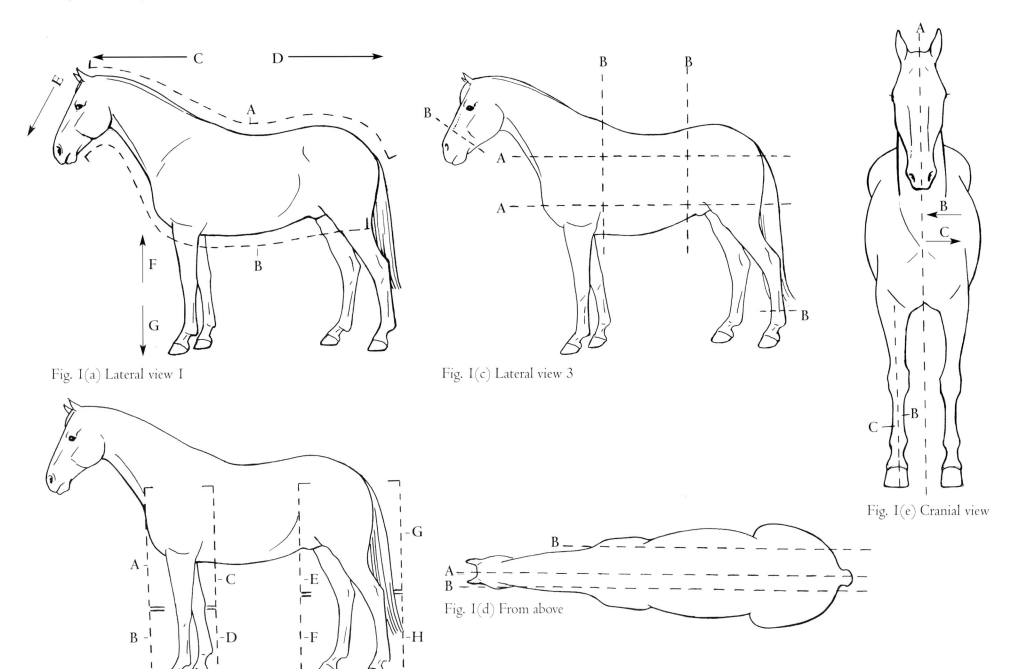

Fig. I(a) Lateral view 1

Fig. I(c) Lateral view 3

Fig. I(e) Cranial view

Fig. I(d) From above

Fig. I(b) Lateral view 2

REGIONS OF THE BODY
(Figure 2)

Identify and colour:

1. Lips
2. Nostrils
3. Face
4. Forehead
5. Cheek
6. Poll
7. Crest
8. Neck
9. Jugular groove
10. Point of shoulder
11. Chest
12. Arm
13. Shoulder
14. Withers
15. Elbow
16. Forearm
17. Knee
18. Forecannon
19. Fetlock
20. Pastern
21. Hoof
22. Girth
23. Thorax or barrel
24. Back
25. Loin
26. Point of hip
27. Abdomen or belly
28. Flank
29. Croup
30. Thigh or quarter
31. Stifle
32. Leg or gaskin
33. Hock
34. Hind cannon
35. Coronet
36. Buttock
37. Dock

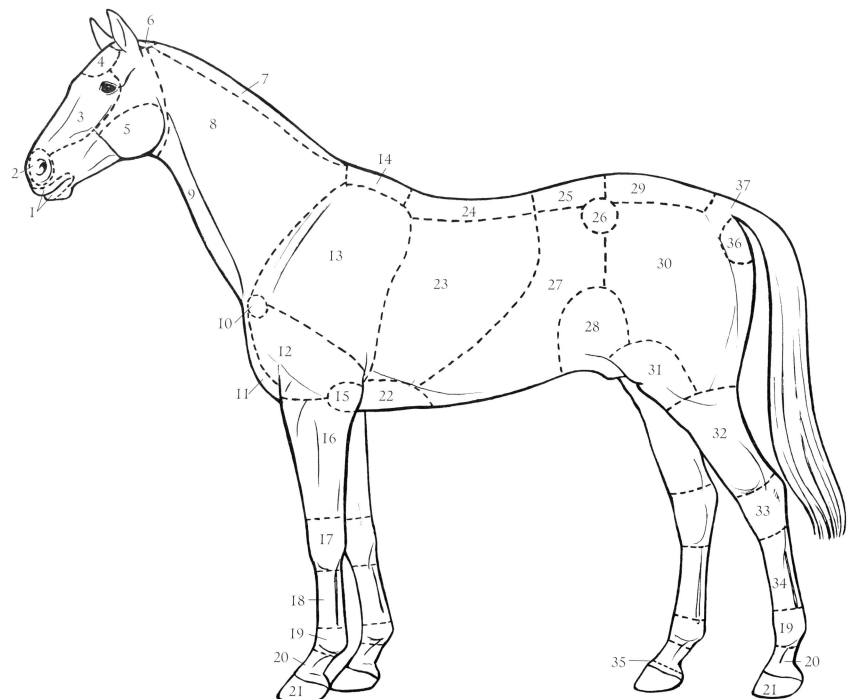

POINTS OF THE HORSE –
Surface Features (Figure 3)

Identify and colour:

1. Nasal peak (rostral ends of nasal bones)
2. Nasal bone
3. Frontal bone
4. Body of mandible (lower jaw)
5. Facial crest
6. Masseter muscle
7. Zygomatic arch
8. Parotid salivary gland
9. Wing of atlas
10. Transverse processes of 3rd–6th cervical vertebrae
11. Jugular groove
12. Trachea (windpipe)
13. Point of shoulder (cranial part of greater tuberosity of humerus)
14. Deltoid tuberosity of humerus
15. Scapular spine
16. Cranial angle of scapula
17. Scapular cartilage
18. Caudal angle of scapula
19. Position of elbow joint
20. Point of elbow (olecranon process of ulna)
21. Lateral styloid process of radius
22. Proximal row of carpal bones
23. Distal row of carpal bones
24. Metacarpal tuberosity
25. Lateral splint bone (lateral metacarpal)
26. Accessory carpal bone
27. Medial splint bone
28. Flexor tendon (superficial and deep digital flexor tendons)
29. Suspensory ligament
30. Xiphoid process of sternum
31. Costal arch
32. Ribs
33. Point of hip (tuber coxae)
34. Patella
35. Tibial tuberosity
36. Tibial crest (cranial margin of tibia)
37. Lateral epicondyle of femur
38. Third trochanter of femur
39. Position of hip joint (greater trochanter of femur)
40. Point of buttock (tuber ischii)
41. Subcutaneous medial surface of tibia
42. Medial malleolus of tibia
43. Medial splint bone
44. Lateral malleolus of tibia
45. Lateral ridge of trochlea of talus (astralgus or tibial tarsal)
46. Point of hock (tuber calcis)
47. Common calcaneal tendon (the aggregate of tendons attached to the hock, including Achilles' tendon)
48. Lateral splint bone

FIGURE 3: POINTS OF THE HORSE – Surface Features

PART 2 – *The Skeleton*

THE SKELETON – Lateral View
(Figure 4)

Label:

A   Vertebrae

B   Tuber coxae (point of hip)

C   Tuber sacrale (point of croup)

D   Tuber ischii (point of buttock)

Identify and colour:

(1)   Skull

(2)   Mandible

(3)   Scapula

(4)   Scapular cartilage

(5)   Humerus

(6)   Sternum

(7)   Radius

(8)   Ulna

(9)   Carpal bones

(10) Lateral splint bone (lateral small metacarpal
      or M4)

(11) Medial splint bone (medial small metacarpal
      or M2)

(12) Cannon bone (large metacarpal or M3)

(13) Pastern bone (1st phalanx)

(14) Proximal sesamoid bones (paired)

(15) Short pastern bone (2nd phalanx or P2)

(16) Pedal bone (3rd phalanx or P3)

(17) Navicular bone (distal sesamoid bone)

(18) Costal cartilages

(19) Ribs

(20) Ilium

(21) Pubis

(22) Ischium

(23) Femur

(24) Patella

(25) Tibia

(26) Fibula

(27) Tarsal bones

(28) Hind cannon (large metatarsal or M3)

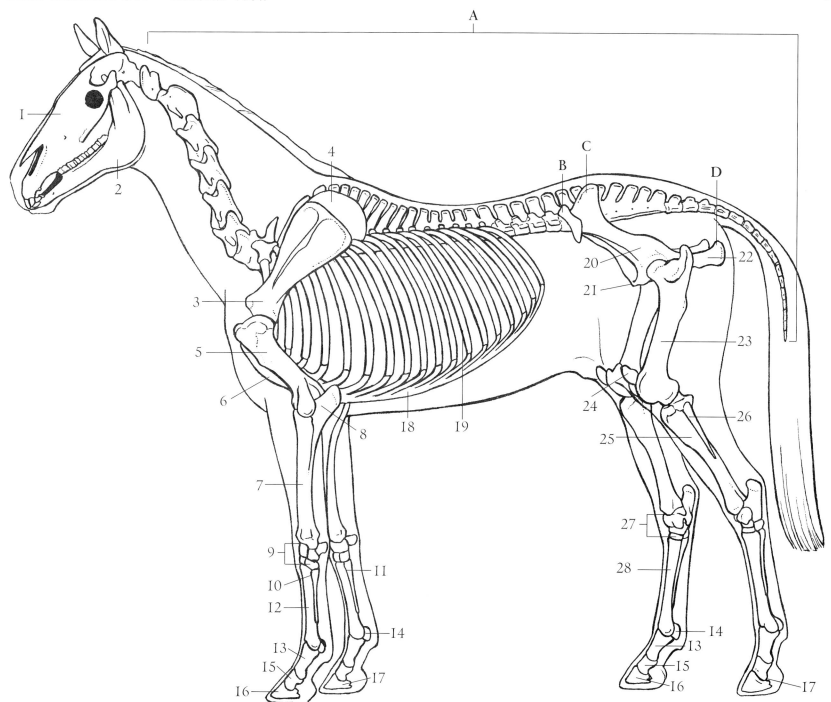

MAJOR PALPABLE SKELETAL FEATURES – Lateral View
(Figure 5)

Identify and colour the skeletal features; locate the position of each on the previous drawing (Figure 4) of the skeleton.

1. Nasal process of incisive bone
2. Nasal peak
3. Infraorbital foramen
4. Facial crest
5. Orbit
6. Zygomatic process of frontal bone
7. Zygomatic arch
8. Temporal line of frontal bone
9. External occipital protuberance
10. Ventral border of mandibular body
11. Angle of mandible
12. Mandibular condyle
13. Wing of atlas
14. Transverse processes of cervical vertebrae
15. Proximal part of cranial border of scapula
16. Dorsal border of scapular cartilage
17. Scapular spine
18. Manubrium of sternum
19. Caudal part of greater tubercle of humerus
20. Cranial part of greater tubercle of humerus
21. Deltoid tuberosity of humerus
22. Lateral (extensor) epicondyle of humerus
23. Lateral tuberosity of radius
24. Olecranon process of ulna
25. Body of sternum
26. Xiphoid cartilage of sternum
27. Costal arch
28. Withers (spinous processes of thoracic vertebrae 3–5)
29. Spinous processes of thoracic vertebra 6 to caudal vertebra 2
30. Sacral tuber of ilium
31. Coxal tuber of ilium
32. Transverse processes of lumbar vertebrae
33. Caudal part of greater trochanter of femur
34. Cranial part of greater trochanter of femur
35. Ischiatic tuber of ischium
36. 3rd trochanter of femur
37. Patella
38. Lateral ridge of femoral trochlea
39. Lateral epicondyle of femur
40. Lateral condyle of tibia and head of fibula
41. Crest of tibia
42. Calcaneal tuber (point of hock)
43. Lateral malleolus of tibia
44. Trochlea of talus
45. Lateral surface of base of 4th metacarpal or metatarsal bone (lateral splint bone)
46. Distal ends of 2nd or 4th metacarpal or metatarsal bone
47. Medial surface of base of 2nd metacarpal or metatarsal bone (medial splint bone)
48. Distal tuberosities of 3rd metacarpal or metatarsal bone
49. Proximal sesamoid bones
50. Proximal tuberosities of 1st phalanx
51. Distal tuberosities of 1st phalanx
52. Proximal border of lateral cartilage of 3rd phalanx
53. Metacarpal tuberosity of 3rd metacarpal
54. Lateral styloid process of radius
55. Accessory carpal bone
56. Medial styloid process of radius
57. Medial malleolus of tibia
58. Medial tuberosity of talus

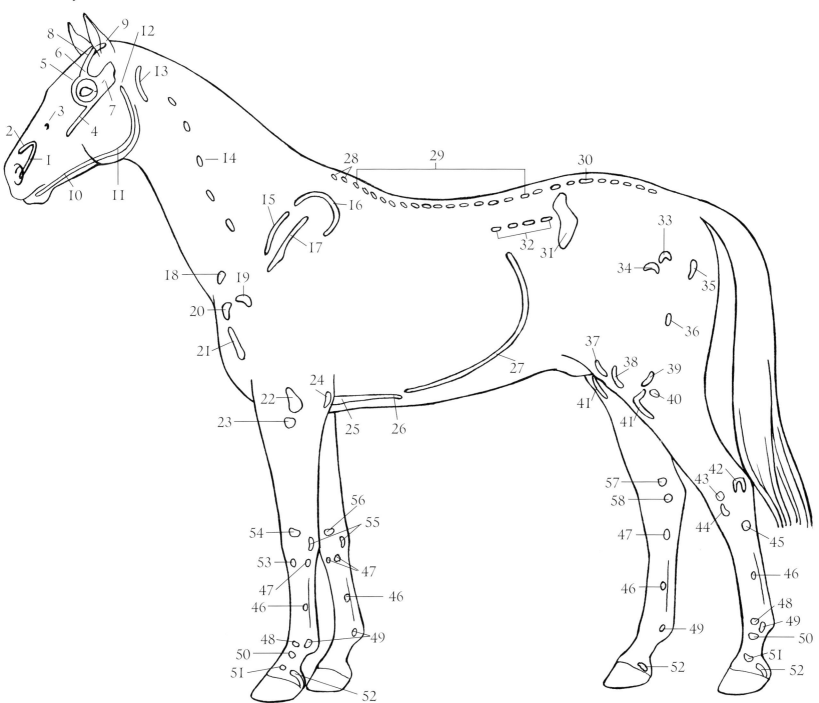

SKELETON AND SURFACE FEATURES FROM ABOVE
(Figure 6)

Fig. 6(a) Skeleton
Label:

A   Atlas (1st cervical vertebra)

B   Axis (2nd cervical vertebra)

C   Cervical vertebrae 3–7

D   Thoracic vertebrae 1–18

E   Lumbar vertebrae

F   Sacrum (5 fused vertebrae)

G   1st caudal vertebra

Identify and colour:

1   Scapula

2   Humerus

3   Scapular cartilage

4   Ribs

5   Pelvic bone

6   Femur

Fig. 6(b) Surface Features
Identify and colour:

1   External parietal crest

2   Wing of atlas

3   Transverse process of cervical vertebrae

4   Lesser tubercle of humerus

5   Cranial part of greater tubercle of humerus

6   Scapular spine

7   Scapular cartilage

8   Spinous processes of thoracic vertebrae

9   Spinous processes of lumbar vertebrae

10 Sacral tuber of ilium

11 Sacral spinous processes

12 Transverse processes of lumbar vertebrae

13 18th rib

14 Coxal tuber of ilium

15 Greater trochanter of femur

16 Ischiatic tuber of ischium

Locate the position of each on the previous drawing (6a) of the skeleton.

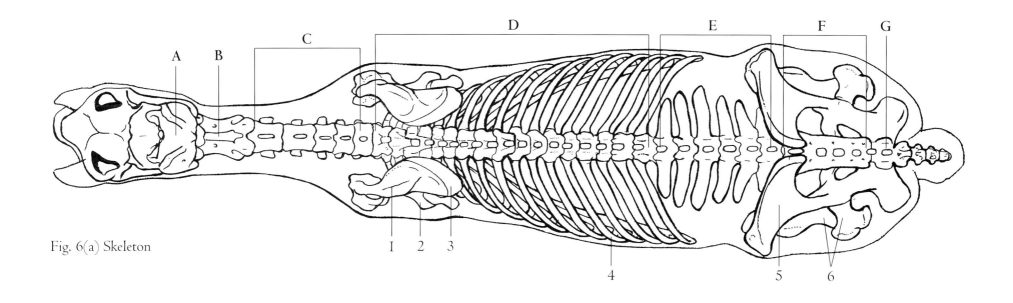

Fig. 6(a) Skeleton

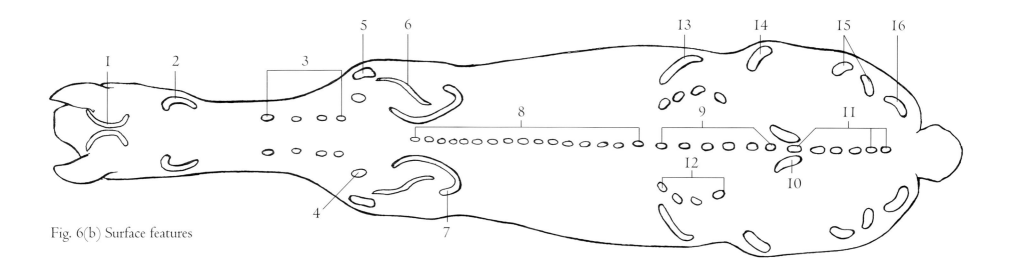

Fig. 6(b) Surface features

VERTEBRAL COLUMN, RIBS AND STERNUM – Lateral Overview and Various Views
(Figure 7)

Fig. 7(a) Lateral Overview

Label:

A   7 Cervical vertebrae

B   18 Thoracic vertebrae

C   6 Lumbar vertebrae

D   5 Sacral vertebrae (fused to form sacrum)

E   15–21 Caudal vertebrae

F   Sternum

Identify and colour.

(1)   Atlas

(2)   Axis

(3)   Caudal articular process   } prevent excessive

(4)   Cranial articular process } torsion

(5)   Intervertebral foramen (for passage of blood vessels and nerves)

(6)   Spinous process

(7)   Transverse process

(8)   Mammillary process

(9)   Neck of rib

(10) Shaft of rib

(11) Costal cartilage

(12) Sternocostal junction

(13) Costochondral junction

(14) Xiphoid cartilage

(15) 8th rib – last true rib (i.e. with direct sternal attachment)

(16) Costal arch (costal cartilage of ribs 9–18 united by elastic tissue)

(17) Ventral sacral foramina

(18) Lateral sacral crest (fused transverse processes of S2–S5)

Figs. 7(b) and (c) Sternum – Dorsal and Lateral View, (d) 1st Ribs, 1st Thoracic Vertebra and Sternum – Cranial View and (e) Ribs, Medial View

Identify and colour the following, matching colours to Fig. 7(a) where appropriate.

NB numbers 7–14 are different views of features that appear in Fig. 7(a).

(7)   Transverse process

(10) Shaft of rib

(11) Costal cartilage

(12) Sternocostal junction

(13) Costochondral junction

(14) Xiphoid cartilage

(19) Xiphoid process

(20) Sternebrae

(21) Manubrium

(22) Manubrial cartilage

(23) Costal facets for 1st ribs

(24) Ventral cartilaginous crest (keel) of sternum

(25) Ribs

(26) Tubercle

(27) Head of rib

(28) Neck of rib

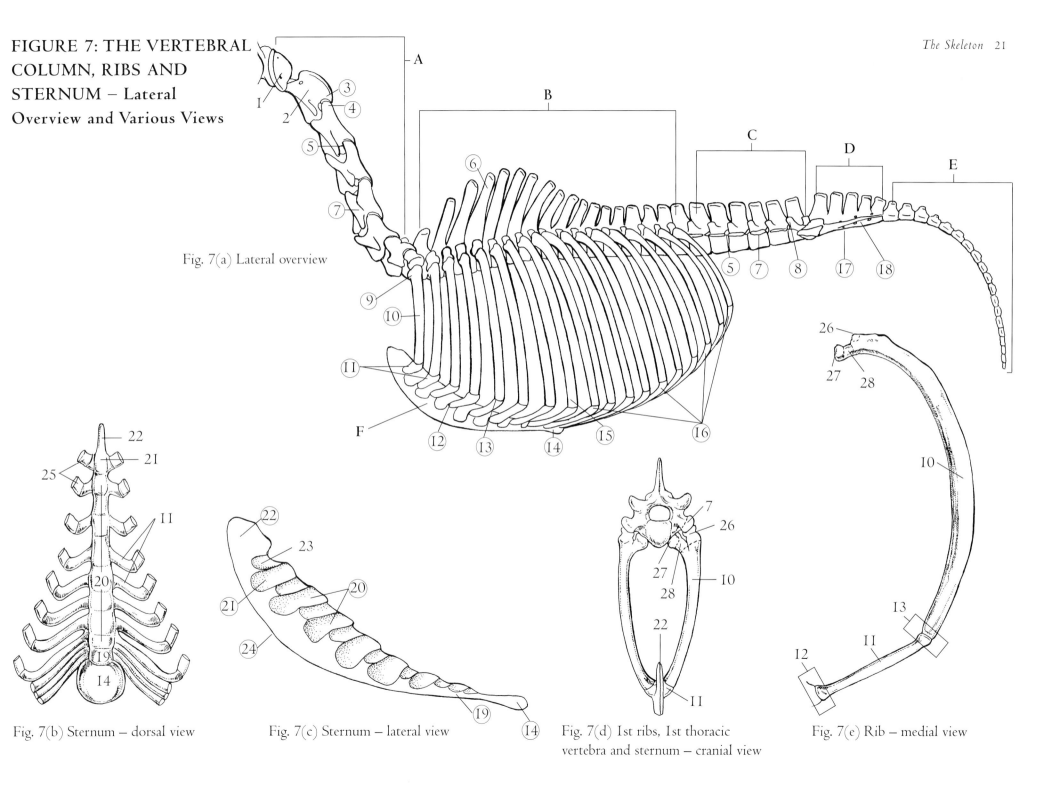

FIGURE 7: THE VERTEBRAL
COLUMN, RIBS AND
STERNUM – Lateral
Overview and Various Views

Fig. 7(a) Lateral overview

Fig. 7(b) Sternum – dorsal view

Fig. 7(c) Sternum – lateral view

Fig. 7(d) 1st ribs, 1st thoracic
vertebra and sternum – cranial view

Fig. 7(e) Rib – medial view

VERTEBRAE AND COMPLETE SPINAL COLUMN – Lateral Overview and Various Views
(Figure 8)

Identify and colour:

(1) Body of vertebra

(2) Arch of vertebra

(3) Vertebral foramen (housing spinal column)

(4) Spinous process

(5) Transverse process

(6) Mammillary process (on thoracic and lumbar vertebrae)

(7) Cranial articular process

(8) Caudal articular process

(9) Transverse canal of cervical vertebra

(10) Costal articular surface on transverse process (for articulation of tubercle of rib)

(11) Costal articular surface on vertebral body (for articulation of head of rib)

(12) Transverse foramen of cervical vertebra

(13) Synovial joint surface for articulation with sacral wing

Locate and indicate the position of each vertebra on the drawing of the complete spinal column.

FIGURE 8: VERTEBRAE AND COMPLETE SPINAL COLUMN –
Lateral Overview and Various Views

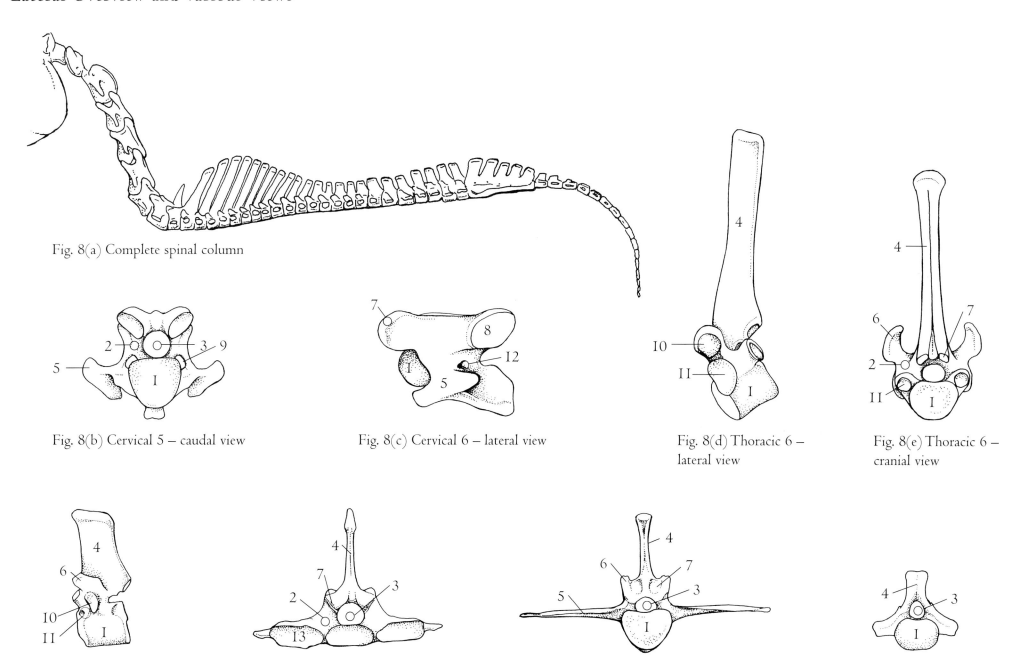

Fig. 8(a) Complete spinal column

Fig. 8(b) Cervical 5 – caudal view

Fig. 8(c) Cervical 6 – lateral view

Fig. 8(d) Thoracic 6 – lateral view

Fig. 8(e) Thoracic 6 – cranial view

Fig. 8(f) Thoracic 16 – lateral view

Fig. 8(g) Lumbar 6 – caudal view

Fig. 8(h) Lumbar 3 – cranial view

Fig. 8(i) Caudal 1 – cranial view

ATLAS, AXIS AND SACRUM – Various Views (Figure 9)

Figs. 9(a), (b) and (c) Atlas and Axis – Lateral, Dorsal and Ventral Views

Label:

A   Atlas

B   Axis

C   Wing of atlas

D   Dorsal arch

Identify and colour:

(1) Spinous process of axis

(2) Transverse process of axis

(3) Cranial articular cavities of atlas

(4) Cranial articular process of axis

(5) Caudal articular process of axis

(6) Odontoid process of axis (developmental remnant of vertebral body of atlas forming basis of atlantoaxial joint)

(7) Intervertebral foramina

(8) Transverse foramina

(9) Ventral spine of axis

Figs. 9(d), (e) and (f) Sacrum – Dorsal, Ventral and Cranial Views

Label:

A Vertebral foramen (contains the spinal cord)

Identify and colour:

(1) Spinous processes

(2) Dorsal sacral foramina (passage of dorsal rami of sacral nerves)

(3) Ventral sacral foramina (passage of ventral rami of sacral nerves)

(4) Lateral sacral crest

(5) Auricular surface of wing of sacrum (forming sacroiliac joint with ilium of pubic bone)

(6) Synovial joint surface of sacrum (articulation with transverse process of 6th lumbar vertebra)

(7) Sacral wing

(8) Cranial articular process

(9) Mammillary process

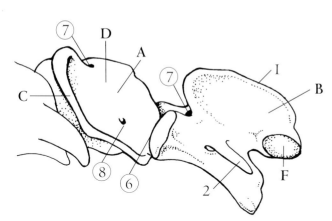

Fig. 9(a) Atlas and axis – lateral view

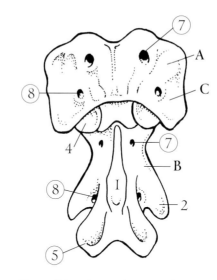

Fig. 9(b) Atlas and axis – dorsal view

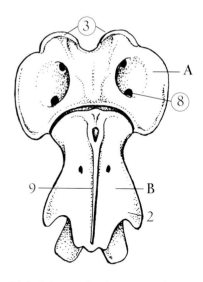

Fig. 9(c) Atlas and axis – ventral view

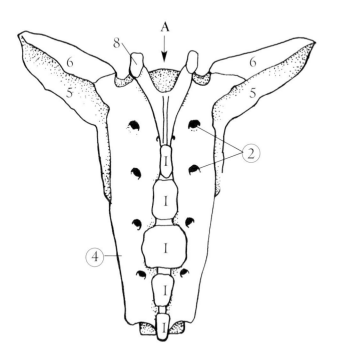

Fig. 9(d) Sacrum – dorsal view

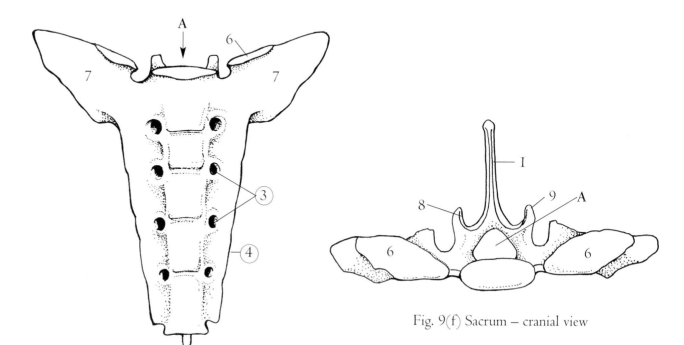

Fig. 9(e) Sacrum – ventral view

Fig. 9(f) Sacrum – cranial view

THE PELVIC GIRDLE –
Dorsal and Lateral Views
(Figure 10)

Label:

A   Ilium

B   Pubis

C   Ischium

D   Sacrum

E   Caudal vertebrae

F   Obturator foramen

Identify and colour:

(1)   Tuber sacrale

(2)   Crest of ilium

(3)   Tuber coxae

(4)   Ischiadic spine

(5)   Acetabulum

(6)   Symphysis pelvis

(7)   Tuber ischii

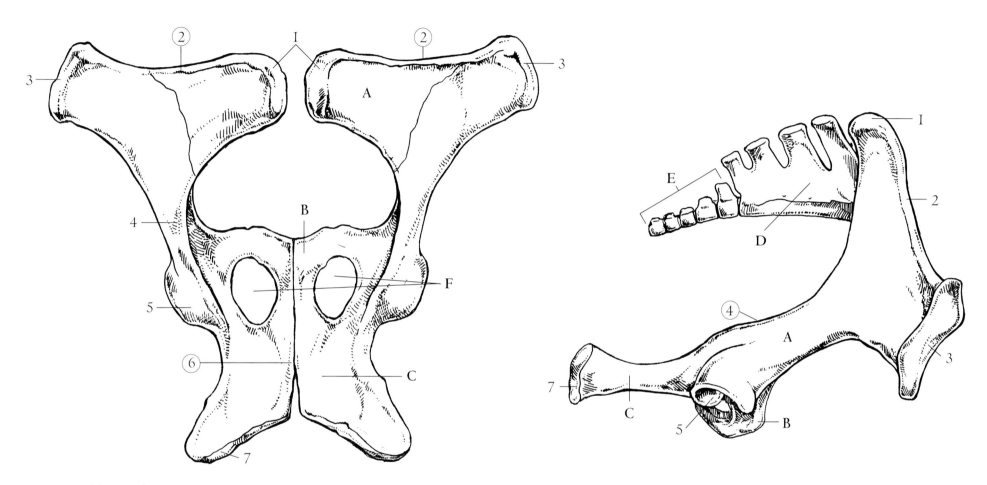

Fig. 10(a) Dorsal view

Fig. 10(b) Lateral view

THE THIGH AND LEG – Cranial and Caudal Views (Figure 11)

Label:

A   Femur

B   Fibula

C   Tibia

D   Intertrochanteric crest

E   Neck

F   Fovea

Identify and colour:

(1)   Head

(2)   Major trochanter

(3)   Minor trochanter

(4)   3rd trochanter

(5)   Patella

(6)   Lateral epicondyle

(7)   Medial epicondyle

(8)   Trochlea

(9)   Lateral condyle

(10)   Medial condyle

(11)   Articular surface for lateral condyle

(12)   Tibial tuberosity

(13)   Intercondylar eminence

(14)   Articular surface for medial condyle

(15)   Lateral malleolus

(16)   Articular surface (tibial cochlea)

(17)   Medial malleolus

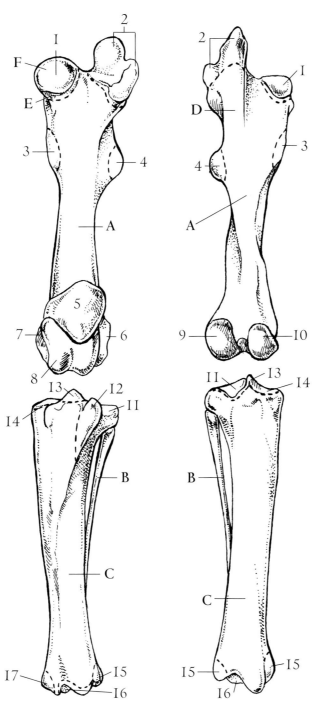

Fig. 11(a) Cranial view

Fig. 11(b) Caudal view

THE HOCK – Dorsal, Plantar and Medial Views
(Figure 12)

Identify and label:

A   Trochlea

B   Talus

C   Calcaneus

D   Calcaneal tuber

E   Sustentaculum tali

Identify and colour:

1   Central tarsal bone

2   1st and 2nd tarsal bones (fused)

3   3rd tarsal bone

4   4th tarsal bone

5   2nd metatarsal bone

6   3rd metatarsal bone

7   4th metatarsal bone

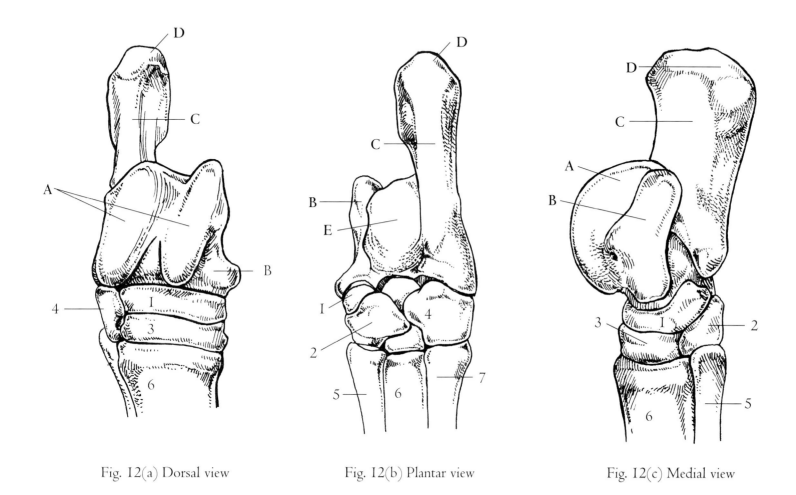

Fig. 12(a) Dorsal view   Fig. 12(b) Plantar view   Fig. 12(c) Medial view

THE SHOULDER, ARM AND FOREARM – Lateral and Medial Views (Figure 13)

Figs. (a) Left Shoulder – Lateral View and (b) Right Shoulder – Medial View

Label:

A Scapula

B Humerus

C Radius

D Ulna

E Olecranon

Identify and colour:

Scapula

1. Scapular cartilage
2. Supraspinous fossa
3. Spine of the scapula
4. Infraspinous fossa
5. Supraglenoid tubercle
6. Serrated face
7. Suprascapular fossa
8. Coracoid process

Humerus

9. Lesser tubercle
10. Major teres tuberosity
11. Medial epicondyle
12. Greater tubercle

13. Head
14. Deltoid tuberosity
15. Olecranon fossa
16. Radial fossa
17. Trochlea of condyle
18. Capitulum of condyle
19. Lateral epicondyle

Radius and ulna

20. Humeral articular surface
21. Anconeal process
22. Olecranon tuberosity
23. Radial tuberosity
24. Carpal articular surface of radius
25. Lateral styloid process

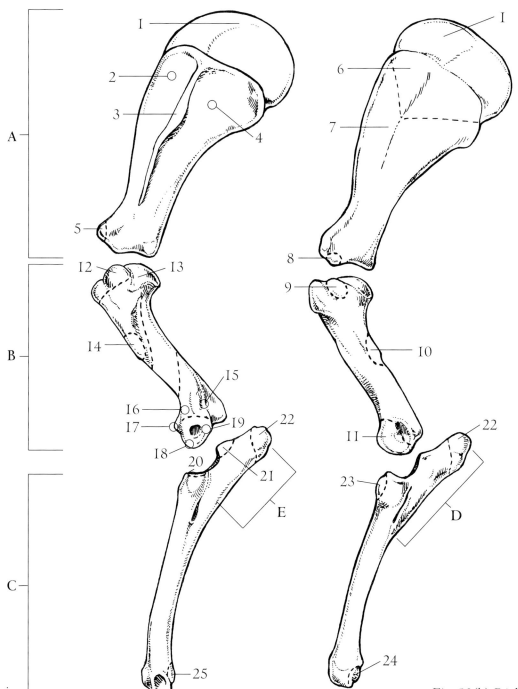

Fig. 13(a) Left shoulder – lateral view

Fig. 13(b) Right shoulder – medial view

THE CARPUS – Dorsal, Lateral and Palmar Views
(Figure 14)

Label:

A   Radius

Identify and colour:

① Radial carpal bone

② Intermediate carpal bone

③ Ulnar carpal bone

④ Accessory carpal bone

⑤ 1st carpal bone (may be absent)

⑥ 2nd carpal bone

⑦ 3rd carpal bone

⑧ 4th carpal bone

⑨ 2nd metacarpal bone

⑩ 3rd metacarpal bone

⑪ 4th metacarpal bone

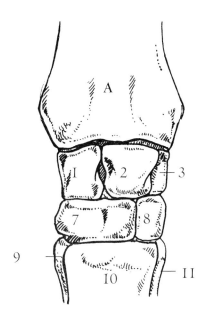

Fig. 14(a) Dorsal view

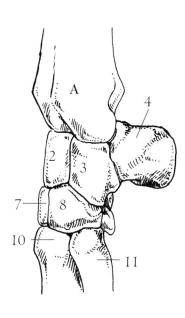

Fig. 14(b) Lateral view

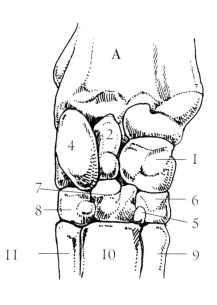

Fig. 14(c) Palmar view

METACARPAL AND DIGITAL BONES – Dorsal and Palmar Views (Figure 15)

Label:

A   Cannon bone (3rd metacarpal)

B   Splint bone (2nd metacarpal – medial)

C   Splint bone (4th metacarpal – lateral)

D   Long pastern bone (1st phalanx)

E   Short pastern bone (2nd phalanx)

F   Navicular bone (distal sesamoid bone)

G   Coffin bone (3rd phalanx)

H   Lateral proximal sesamoid bone

I   Medial proximal sesamoid bone

Identify and colour:

①   Metacarpal tuberosity

②   Ridge on distal articular surface

③   Extensor process of 1st phalanx

④   Articular surface of navicular bone

⑤   Flexor surface of navicular bone

⑥   Extensor process of coffin bone

⑦   Lateral cartilages

⑧   Flexor surface of coffin bone

⑨   Semilunar line

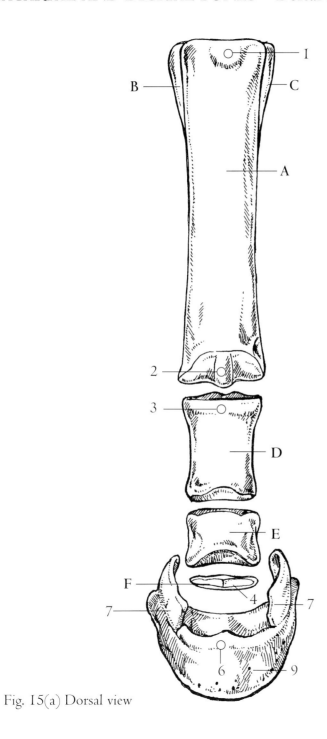

Fig. I5(a) Dorsal view

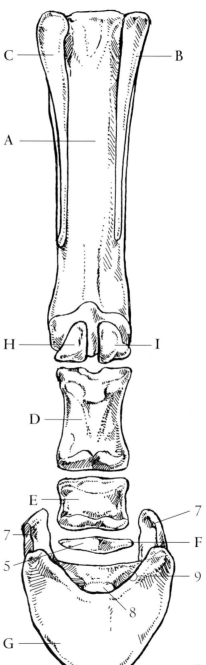

Fig. I5(b) Palmar view

THE SKULL – Lateral, Ventral and Cranial Views
(Figure 16)

Fig. 16(a) Right Lateral View
Label:

A   Incisive bone

B   Nasal bone

C   Frontal bone

D   Lacrimal bone

E   Zygomatic bone

F   Parietal bone

G   Temporal bone

H   Mandible

I   Maxilla

J   Zygomatic arch

K   Zygomatic process

L   Facial crest

Identify and colour:

(1)   Mental foramen

(2)   Infraorbital foramen

(3)   Supraorbital foramen

(4)   Nuchal crest

(5)   Occipital condyle

(6)   Jugular process bone

(7)   External acoustic meatus (around which auricular cartilage is attached and across which the eardrum is stretched in life)

Fig. 16(b) Ventral View, Mandible Removed
Label:

A   Occipital bone

B   Temporal bone

C   Basisphenoid bone

D   Vomer

E   Zygomatic bone

F   Palatine bone

G   Maxilla

H   Incisive bone

Identify and colour:

(1)   Occipital condyle

(2)   Jugular process bone

(3)   Foramen lacerum

(4)   Orbital fissure

(5)   Caudal alar foramen

(6)   Hamulus of pterygoid bone

(7)   Incisive canal

(8)   Molar teeth

(9)   Premolar teeth

(10)   Canine teeth

(11)   Incisor teeth

Fig. 16(c) Cranial View
Identify, label and colour:

A   Parietal bone

B   Frontal bone

C   Nasal bone

D   Maxilla

E   Incisive bone

F   Lacrimal bone

G   Zygomatic bone

H   Nuchal crest

I   Coronoid process of mandible in external fossa

J   Supraorbital foramen

K   Infraorbital foramen

L   Incisive foramen

M   Nasal peak (rostral end of nasal bones)

N   Incisor teeth

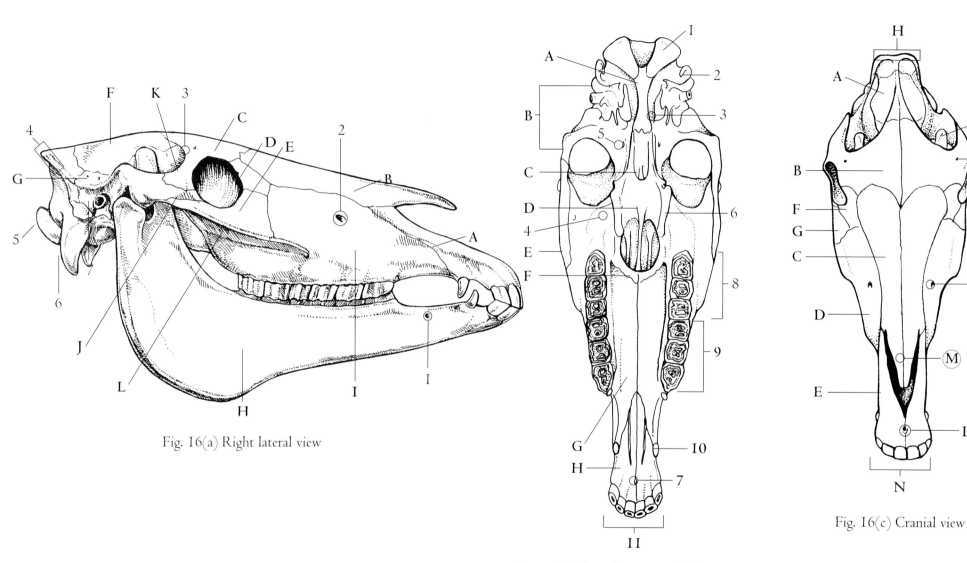

Fig. 16(a) Right lateral view

Fig. 16(b) Ventral view, mandible removed

Fig. 16(c) Cranial view

SKELETON AND SURFACE FEATURES – Cranial View
(Figure 17)

Fig. 17(a) Skeleton

Identify and colour:

(1) Frontal bone

(2) Nasal bone

(3) Facial crest

(4) Nasal peak

(5) Mandible

(6) Scapula

(7) Cervical vertebrae

(8) Humerus

(9) Sternum

(10) Radius

(11) Carpal bones

(12) Large metacarpal (M3 or forecannon)

(13) 1st phalanx (long pastern bone)

(14) 2nd phalanx (short pastern bone)

(15) 3rd phalanx (pedal bone)

Fig. 17(b) Surface Features and Joints

Identify and colour:

(1) External occipital protuberance

(2) Zygomatic arch

(3) Facial crest

(4) Temporal line of frontal bone

(5) Nasal process of incisive bone

(6) Nasal peak

(7) Scapular cartilage

(8) Spine of scapula

(9) Supraglenoid tuberosity of scapula

(10) Lesser tubercle of humerus

(11) Cranial part of greater tubercle of humerus

(12) Deltoid tuberosity of humerus

(13) Lateral epicondyle of humerus

(14) Medial epicondyle of humerus

(15) Lateral radial tuberosity

(16) Medial radial tuberosity

(17) Lateral styloid process of radius

(18) Medial styloid process of radius

(19) 2nd metacarpal bone

(20) Metacarpal tuberosity

(21) 3rd metacarpal bone

(22) 1st phalanx

Locate the following joints on Fig. 17(a) Skeleton and label them:

A   Scapulohumeral (shoulder) joint

B   Cubital (elbow) joint

C   Antebrachiocarpal (knee) joint

D   Metacarpophalangeal (fetlock) joint

E   Proximal interphalangeal (pastern) joint

F   Distal interphalangeal (coffin) joint

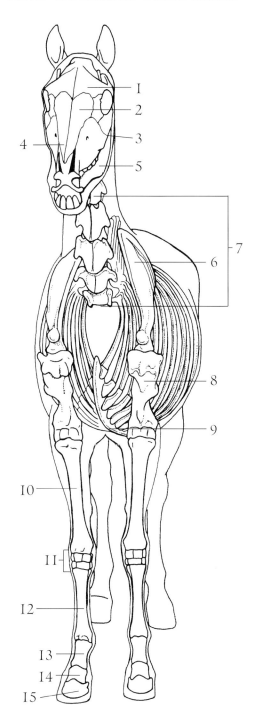

Fig. 17(a) Skeleton

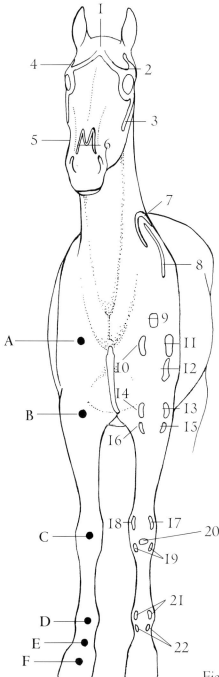

Fig. 17(b) Surface features and joints

SKELETON AND SURFACE FEATURES – Caudal View
(Figure 18)

Fig. 18(a) Skeleton

Identify and colour:

1. Os coxae (pelvic bone)
2. Caudal vertebrae
3. Femur
4. Patella
5. Fibula
6. Tibia
7. Tarsal bones
8. Small metatarsal M4, or lateral splint bone
9. Small metatarsal M2, or medial splint bone
10. Large metatarsal M3, or hind cannon
11. Proximal sesamoid bones
12. 1st phalanx (long pastern bone)
13. 2nd phalanx (short pastern bone)
14. 3rd phalanx (pedal bone)
15. Distal sesamoid bone

Fig. 18(b) Surface Features and Joints

Identify and colour:

1. Sacral spinous processes
2. Sacral tuber of ilium (point of croup)
3. Coxal tuber of ilium (point of haunch)
4. Caudal part of greater femoral trochanter
5. Ischiatic tuber of ischium (point of buttock)

6. Lateral epicondyle of femur
7. Medial epicondyle of femur
8. Head of fibula
9. Medial tibial condyle
10. Calcaneal tuber (point of hock)
11. Lateral malleolus of tibia
12. Bases of splint bones
13. Medial malleolus of tibia
14. Talus (tibial tarsal bone)
15. Proximal plantar sesamoid bones
16. Lateral cartilages
17. Buttons of medial and radial splint bones

The coloured surface features should also be located on Fig.18(a).

Locate the following joints on Fig. 18(a) Skeleton and label them:

A   Hip joint

B   Stifle joint

C   Crurotarsal joint

D   Fetlock

E   Pastern joint

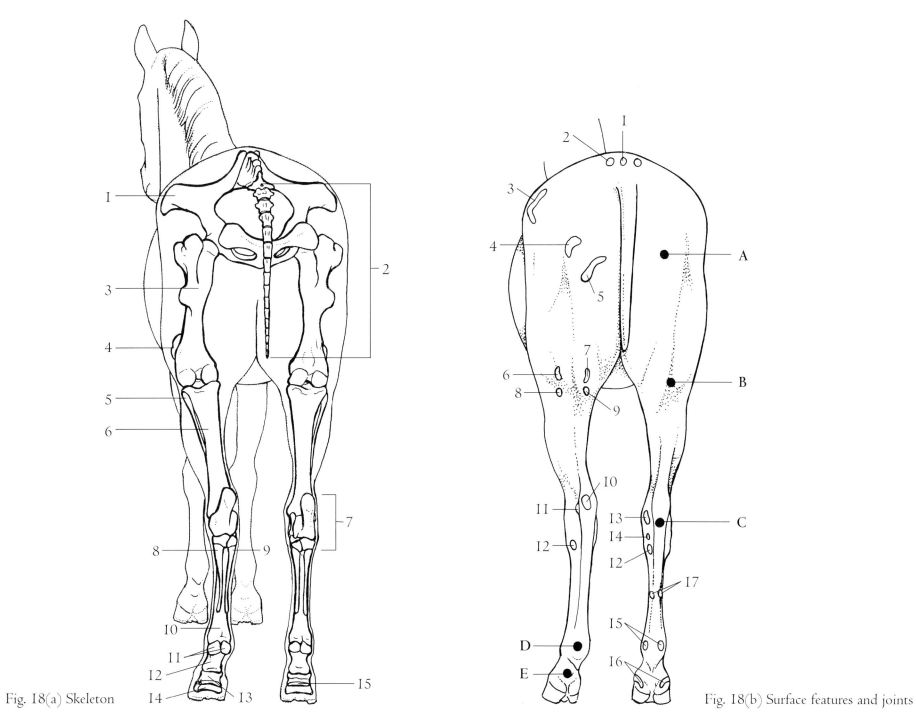

Fig. 18(a) Skeleton

Fig. 18(b) Surface features and joints

PART 3 – *Ligaments, Muscles and Tendons*

LIGAMENTS OF THE SKELETON – Lateral View
(Figure 19)

Identify and colour:

1. Lateral ligament of jaw joint
2. Caudal ligament of jaw joint
3. Supraspinous ligament
4. Lamellar part of nuchal ligament
5. Capsular ligament of shoulder joint
6. Medial collateral ligament of elbow joint
7. Medial transverse radioulnar ligament
8. Lateral collateral ligament of elbow joint
9. Medial collateral ligament of carpal joint
10. Suspensory ligament
11. Medial collateral ligament of fetlock joint
12. Distal or inferior sesamoidean ligament
13. Lateral collateral ligament of carpal joint
14. Distal ligament of the accessory carpal bone
15. Lateral collateral sesamoidean ligament
16. Lateral collateral ligament of pastern joint
17. Lateral collateral ligament of coffin joint
18. Dorsal sacroiliac ligament
19. Lateral sacroiliac ligament
20. Sacrosciatic ligament
21. Capsular ligament of hip joint
22. Medial femoropatellar ligament
23. Medial patellar ligament
24. Medial collateral ligament of stifle joint
25. Lateral femoropatellar ligament
26. Lateral collateral ligament of stifle joint
27. Middle patellar ligament
28. Lateral patellar ligament
29. Medial collateral ligament of tarsal joint
30. Branches of medial collateral ligaments
31. Plantar ligament
32. Lateral collateral ligament of tarsal joint
33. Ligament connecting talus and calcaneus
34. Suspensory ligament of navicular bone

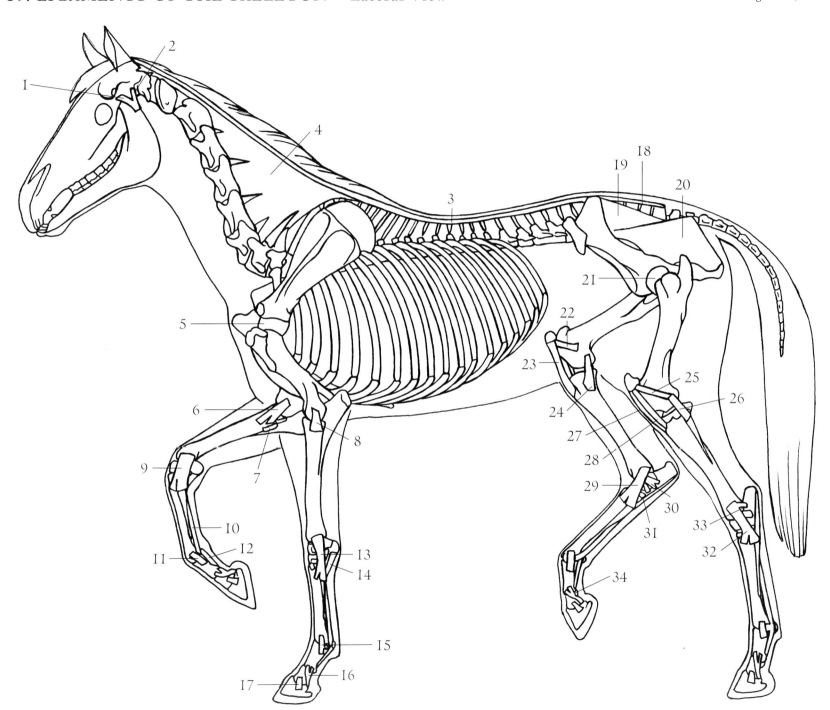

LIGAMENTS OF THE PELVIS AND VERTEBRAE – Various Views (Figure 20)

Figs. (a) Accessory Ligaments of the Hip Joints – Ventral View and (b) Sacrosciatic Ligaments – Dorsal View

Identify and colour:

1. Ventral sacroiliac ligament
2. Sacrosciatic ligament
3. Accessory femoral ligament
4. Articular capsule (capsular ligament) of hip joint
5. Ligament of femoral head (round ligament)
6. Transverse acetabular ligament
7. Dorsal sacroiliac ligament

Figs. (c) Ligaments of the Spine – Median Section and (d) Ligaments of the Rib Heads – Cranial View

Identify and colour:

1. Supraspinous ligament (linking summit of spinous processes to trunk)
2. Costotransverse ligament (ligament of rib tubercle)
3. Intra-articular ligament of rib head
4. Radiate ligament of costal head
5. Ventral longitudinal ligament
6. Dorsal longitudinal ligament
7. Interspinal ligaments
8. Interarcuate ligaments

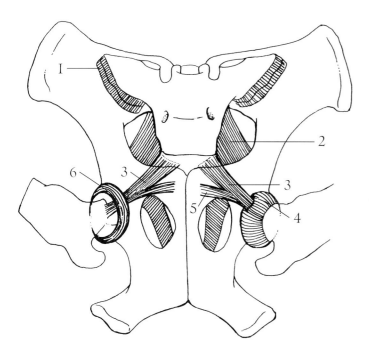

Fig. 20(a) Accessory ligaments of the hip joints – ventral view

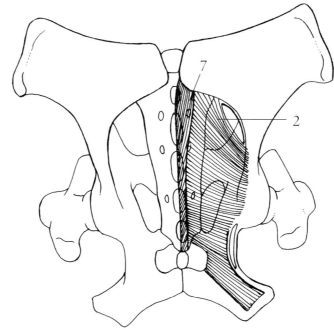

Fig. 20(b) Sacrosciatic ligaments – dorsal view

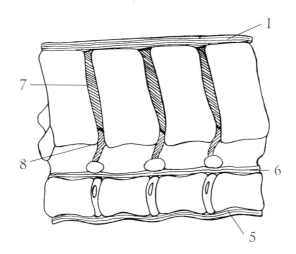

Fig. 20(c) Ligaments of the spine – median section

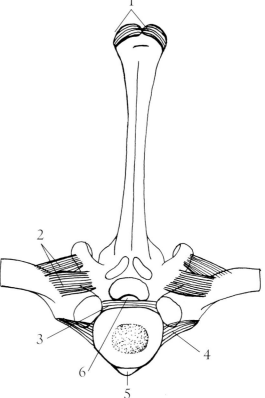

Fig. 20(d) Ligaments of the rib heads – cranial view

LIGAMENTS OF THE LOWER LIMB AND FOOT – Various Views (Figure 21)

Identify and colour:

1. Medial collateral carpal ligament
2. Lateral collateral carpal ligament
3. Intercarpal ligaments
4. Carpometacarpal ligaments
5. Medial and lateral collateral ligaments of pastern joint
6. Extensor branches of suspensory ligament
7. Medial and lateral chondrocompedal ligaments
8. Medial and lateral collateral ligaments of pastern joint
9. Suspensory navicular ligaments
10. Medial and lateral chondrocoronal ligaments
11. Medial and lateral collateral ligaments of coffin joint
12. Medial and lateral collateral ligaments of fetlock joint
13. Common digital extensor tendon (cut)
14. Proximal ligament of accessory carpal bone
15. Distal ligaments of accessory carpal bone
16. Suspensory ligaments (see also ㉖)
17. Medial and lateral collateral sesamoidean ligaments of fetlock joint
18. Oblique distal sesamoidean ligaments
19. Straight distal sesamoidean ligament
20. Abaxial palmar ligament of pastern joint
21. Medial and lateral chondroungular ligaments
22. Superficial digital flexor tendon (cut)
23. Intersesamoidean ligament
24. Distal navicular ligament
25. Cruciate distal sesamoidean ligaments
26. Suspensory ligament bifurcation
27. Short distal sesamoidean ligaments
28. Axial palmar ligament of pastern joint

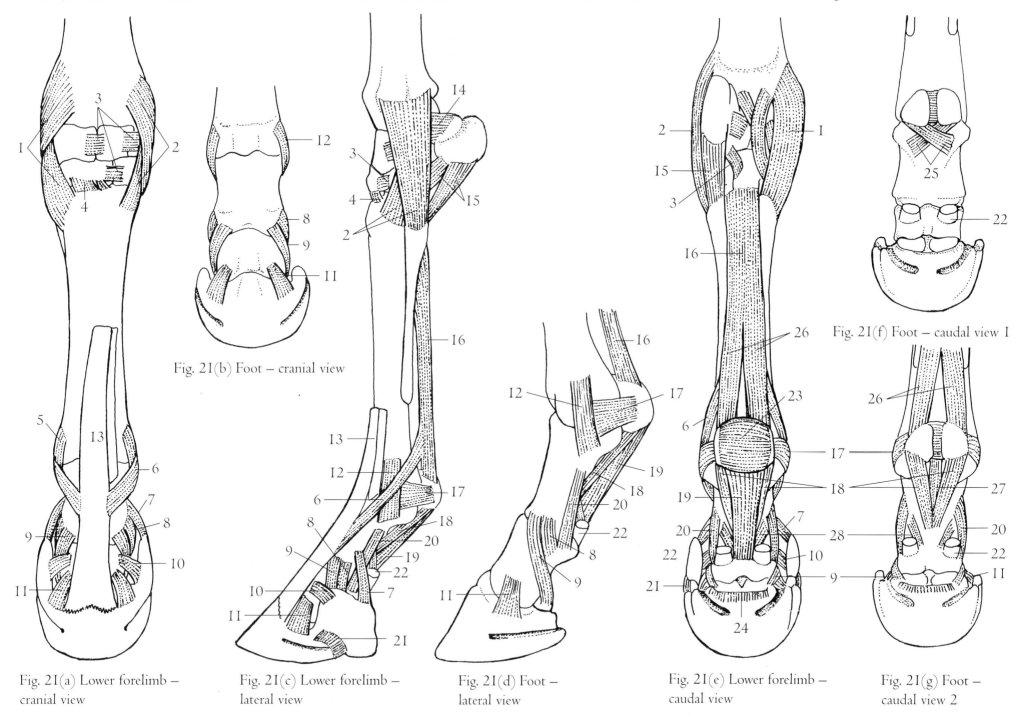

Fig. 21(b) Foot – cranial view

Fig. 21(f) Foot – caudal view 1

Fig. 21(a) Lower forelimb – cranial view

Fig. 21(c) Lower forelimb – lateral view

Fig. 21(d) Foot – lateral view

Fig. 21(e) Lower forelimb – caudal view

Fig. 21(g) Foot – caudal view 2

LIGAMENTS OF THE STIFLE JOINT – Medial, Cranial and Lateral Views
(Figure 22)

Label:

A   Patella

B   Peripatellar cartilage

C   Tibial tuberosity

D   Fibula

Identify and colour:

(1) Medial patellar ligament

(2) Medial ridge of trochlea

(3) Middle patellar ligament

(4) Lateral patellar ligament

(5) Medial collateral ligament

(6) Medial meniscus

(7) Lateral meniscus

(8) Lateral collateral ligament

(9) Medial femoropatellar ligament

(10) Lateral femoropatellar ligament

FIGURE 22: LIGAMENTS OF THE STIFLE JOINT –
Medial, Cranial and Lateral Views

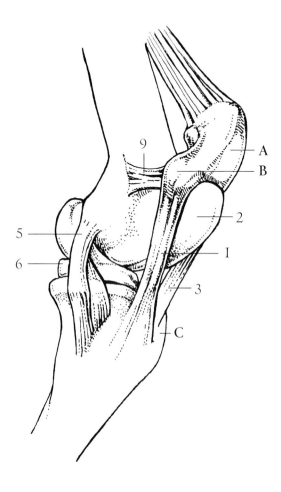

Fig. 22(a) Medial view

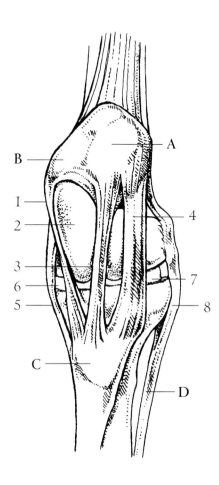

Fig. 22(b) Cranial view

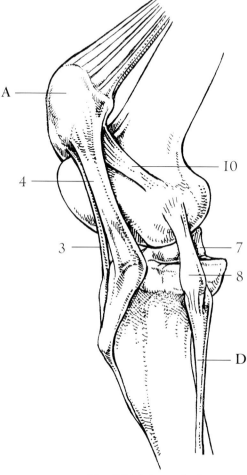

Fig. 22(c) Lateral view

LIGAMENTS OF THE HOCK –
Cranial, Lateral and Caudal Views
(Figure 23)

Label:

A   Trochlea of talus

B   Calcaneal tuber

C   Sustentaculum tali

Identify and colour:

1 Long and short medial collateral tarsal ligaments

2 Long and short lateral collateral tarsal ligaments

3 Dorsal tarsal ligament

4 Tarsometatarsal ligaments

5 Long plantar ligament

6 Plantar tarsal ligaments

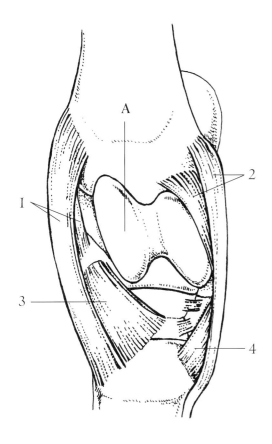

Fig. 23(a) Cranial view

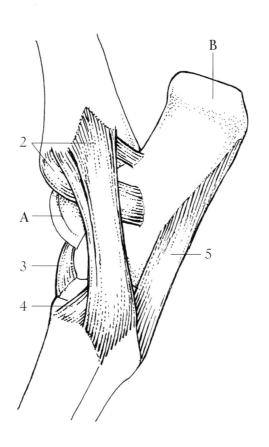

Fig. 23(b) Lateral view

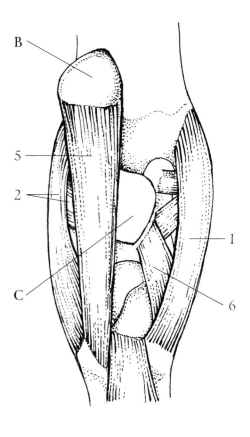

Fig. 23(c) Caudal view

SUPERFICIAL MUSCLES –
Lateral View (Figure 24)

Label:

A   Lateral crural fascia

B   Gluteal fascia

C   Thoracolumbar fascia

Identify and colour:

(1)   Lateral nostril dilator muscles

(2)   Levator muscle of upper lip and wing of nostril

(3)   Superior labial levator muscle

(4)   Orbicularis oculi muscle

(5)   Levator muscle of medial angle of eye

(6)   Masseter muscle

(7)   Auricular muscle

(8)   Cervical part of rhomboid muscle

(9)   Splenius muscle

(10) Cervical ventral serrate muscle

(11) Cervical part of trapezius muscle

(12) Thoracic part of trapezius muscle

(13) Latissimus dorsi muscle

(14) Sternomandibular muscle

(15) Cutaneous colli muscle

(16) Brachiocephalic muscle

(17) Deltoid muscle

(18) Cranial superficial pectoral muscle

(19) Brachial triceps muscle

(20) Brachial muscle

(21) Radial carpal extensor muscle and tendon

(22) Common digital extensor muscle and tendon

(23) Lateral digital extensor muscle and tendon

(24) Lateral carpal flexor muscle and tendon

(25) Deep digital flexor muscle and tendon

(26) Thoracic ventral serrate muscle

(27) Caudal deep pectoral muscle

(28) External intercostal muscles

(29) External abdominal oblique muscle

(30) Tensor muscle of lateral femoral fascia

(31) Superficial gluteal muscle

(32) Semitendinosus muscle

(33) Short tail levator muscle

(34) Biceps femoris

(35) Long digital extensor muscle and tendon

(36) Lateral digital extensor muscle and tendon

(37) Deep digital flexor muscle and tendon

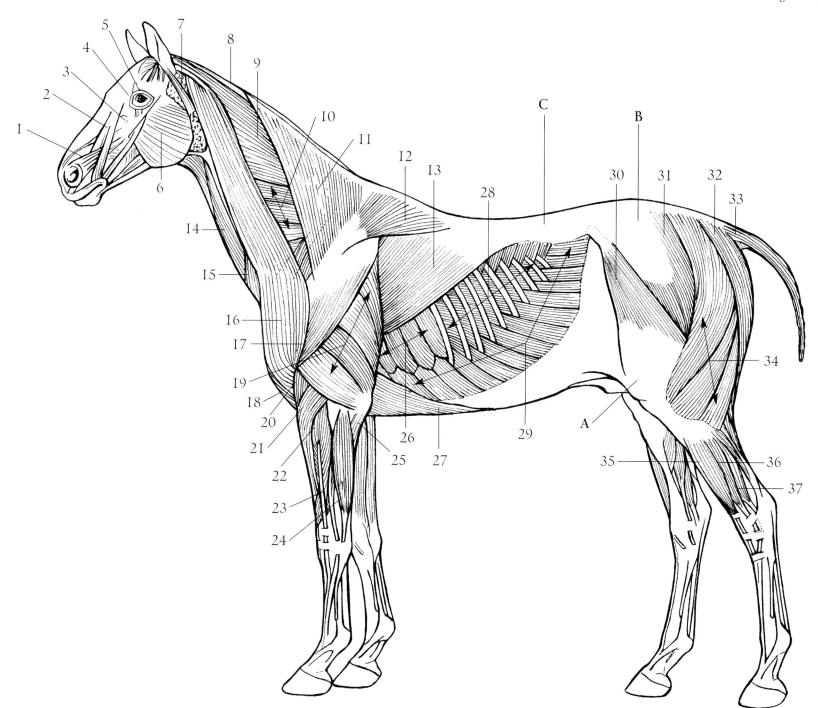

DEEP MUSCLES PART I – Lateral Overview and Medial Views of Shoulder and Hindquarter (Figure 25)

Fig. 25(a) Lateral Overview

Identify and colour:

1. Levator muscle of nostril wing and upper lip
2. Sphincter muscle of mouth
3. Zygomatic muscle
4. Depressor muscle of lower lip
5. Superficial component of masseter muscle
6. Temporal muscle
7. Splenius muscle
8. Sternomandibular muscle
9. Omohyoid muscle
10. Rhomboid muscle
11. Subclavius muscle
12. Supraspinous muscle
13. Infraspinous muscle
14. Deltoid muscle
15. Triceps muscle
16. Cranial dorsal serrate muscle
17. Caudal dorsal serrate muscle
18. Thoracic part of ventral serrate muscle
19. Middle gluteal muscle
20. Deep gluteal muscle
21. Semitendinosus muscle
22. Tendon of internal obturator muscle
23. Quadratus femoris muscle
24. Semimembranosus muscle
25. Adductor muscle
26. Lateral head of gastrocnemius muscle
27. Rectus femoris muscle
28. Lateral vastus muscle
29. Popliteal muscle
30. Deep digital flexor muscle
31. Cranial tibial muscle
32. Radial carpal extensor muscle
33. Radial carpal flexor muscle
34. Ulnar carpal flexor muscle

Fig. 25(b) Right Shoulder and Forearm (Removed from Body) – Medial View

Identify and colour:

1. Scapular cartilage
2. Serrated face of scapula (attachment for ventral serrate muscle)
3. Subscapular muscle
4. Supraspinous muscle
5. Latissimus dorsi muscle
6. Teres major muscle
7. Coracobrachial muscle
8. Triceps muscle
9. Tensor muscle of antebrachial fascia
10. Biceps brachii muscle
11. Deep digital flexor muscle
12. Lacertus fibrosus (tendoligamentous band linking biceps tendon with radial carpal extensor tendon, important in forelimb 'stay mechanism')
13. Brachial muscle
14. Radial carpal extensor muscle
15. Ulnar carpal flexor muscle
16. Radial carpal flexor muscle

Fig. 25(c) Hindquarter – Medial View

Identify and colour:

1. Psoas minor muscle
2. Psoas major component of iliopsoas muscle
3. Iliacus component of iliopsoas muscle
4. Tensor muscle of lateral fascia of thigh
5. Pectineus muscle
6. Sartorius muscle
7. Medial vastus muscle
8. Gracilis muscle
9. Tail depressor muscle
10. Coccygeal muscle
11. Lavator ani muscle
12. Semimembranosus muscle
13. Semitendinosus muscle
14. Internal obturator muscle
15. Medial head of gastrocnemius muscle
16. Symphyseal tendon

FIGURE 25: DEEP MUSCLES PART I – Lateral Overview and Medial Views of Shoulder and Hindquarter

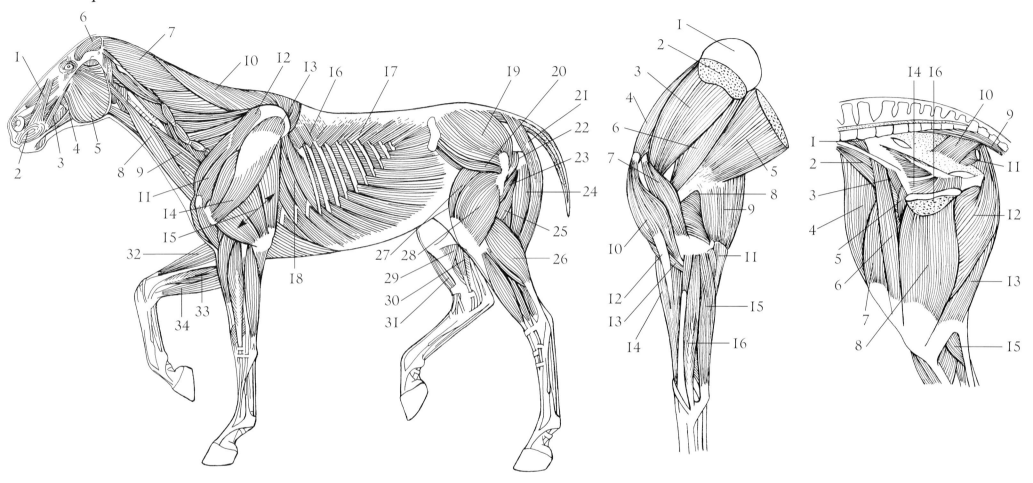

Fig. 25(a) Lateral overview

Fig. 25(b) Right shoulder and forearm (removed from body) – medial view

Fig. 25(c) Hindquarter – medial view

DEEP MUSCLES PART 2 – Lateral View without Left Shoulder, Dissections of Shoulder and Medial View of Hindquarter

(Figure 26)

Fig. 26(a) Lateral View without Left Shoulder

Identify and colour:

1. Levator muscle of upper lip
2. Levator muscle of upper lip and nostril wing
3. Transverse nasal muscle
4. Sphincter muscle of mouth
5. Buccinator muscle (buccal part)
6. Depressor muscle of lower lip
7. Buccinator muscle (molar part)
8. Temporal muscle
9. Occipitomandibular part of digastric muscle
10. Splenius muscle
11. Thyropharyngeal muscle
12. Cricopharyngeal muscle
13. Sternohyoid and sternothyroid muscle
14. Longus capitus and longus colli muscles
15. Omohyoid muscle
16. Trachea
17. Cervical intertransverse muscles
18. Scalene muscle
19. Cervical rhomboid muscle
20. Thoracic rhomboid muscle
21. Subclavius muscle

22. Rectus thoracis muscle
23. Descending superficial pectoral muscle
24. Caudal deep pectoral muscle
25. Transverse superficial pectoral muscle
26. Thoracic ventral serrate muscle
27. Cranial dorsal serrate muscle
28. External intercostal muscles
29. External abdominal oblique muscles
30. Caudal dorsal serrate muscle
31. Iliopsoas muscle
32. Deep gluteal muscle
33. Coccygeus muscle
34. Internal obturator muscle and tendon
35. Lateral vastus muscle
36. Quadratus femoris muscle
37. Tail levator, flexor and depressor muscles
38. Lateral head of gastrocnemius muscle
39. Soleus muscle
40. Cranial tibial muscle
41. Long digital extensor muscle
42. Lateral digital extensor muscle
43. Deep digital flexor muscle
44. Ulnar carpal flexor muscle
45. Radial carpal extensor muscle
46. Radial carpal flexor muscle

Figs. 26(b) Muscles of Left Shoulder and Upper Limb and (c) Further Dissection

Identify and colour:

1. Supraspinous muscle

2. Infraspinous muscle
3. Long head of triceps muscle
4. Biceps brachii muscle
5. Brachial muscle
6. Teres major muscle
7. Medial head of triceps muscle
8. Deep digital flexor muscle
9. Lateral ulnar muscle
10. Radial carpal extensor muscle
11. Common digital extensor muscle
12. Lateral digital extensor muscle
13. Anconeal muscle

Fig. 26(d) Hindquarter – Medial View

Identify and colour:

1. Psoas minor muscle
2. Psoas major muscle
3. Iliacus muscle
4. Internal obturator muscle and tendon
5. Rectus femoris muscle
6. Pectineus muscle
7. Medial vastus muscle
8. Adductor muscle
9. Tail depressor muscle
10. Coccygeus muscle
11. Levator ani muscle
12. Semimembranosus muscle
13. Semitendinosus muscle
14. Popliteal muscle
15. Sacrosciatic muscle

FIGURE 26 DEEP MUSCLES PART 2 – Lateral View without Left Shoulder, Dissections of Shoulder and Medial View of Hindquarter

Ligaments, Muscles and Tendons 59

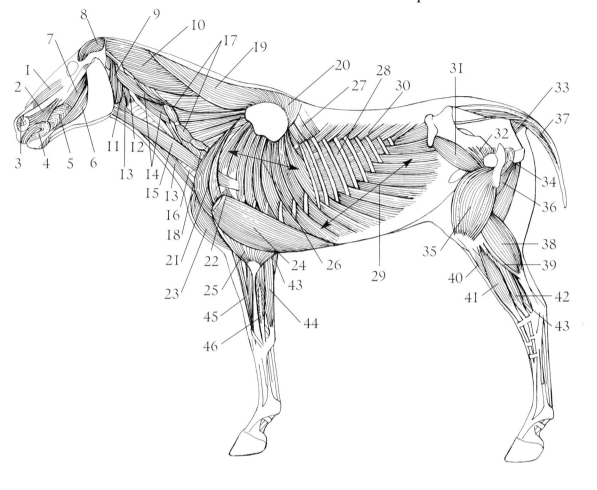

Fig. 26(a) Lateral view without left shoulder (removed)

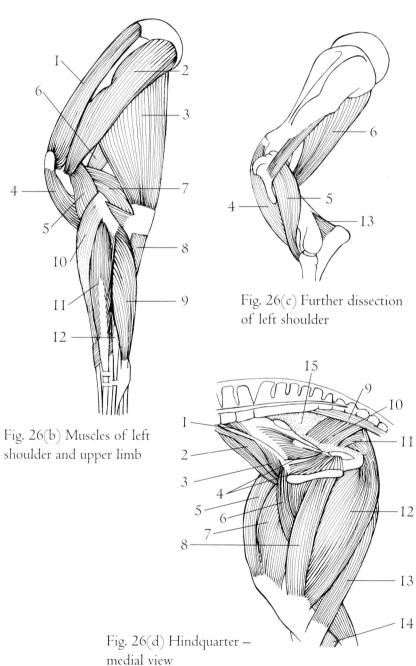

Fig. 26(b) Muscles of left shoulder and upper limb

Fig. 26(c) Further dissection of left shoulder

Fig. 26(d) Hindquarter – medial view

DEEP MUSCLES PART 3 –
Axial Musculature in Lateral
View (I) (Figure 27)

Identify and colour:

1. Mylohyoid muscle
2. Digastric muscle
3. Medial pterygoid muscle
4. Lateral pterygoid muscle
5. Occipitohyoid muscle
6. Occipitomandibular muscle
7. Thyropharyngeal muscle
8. Cricopharyngeal muscle
9. Sternohyoid muscle
10. Sternothyroid muscle
11. Splenius muscle
12. Cranial dorsal serrate muscle
13. Caudal dorsal serrate muscle
14. Coccygeus muscle
15. Iliopsoas muscle (cut through)
16. External abdominal oblique muscle
17. External intercostal muscle
18. Rectus abdominis muscle
19. Rectus thoracis muscle
20. Scalene muscle
21. Sacrosciatic ligament
22. Lateral sacral crest
23. Cervical intertransverse muscles

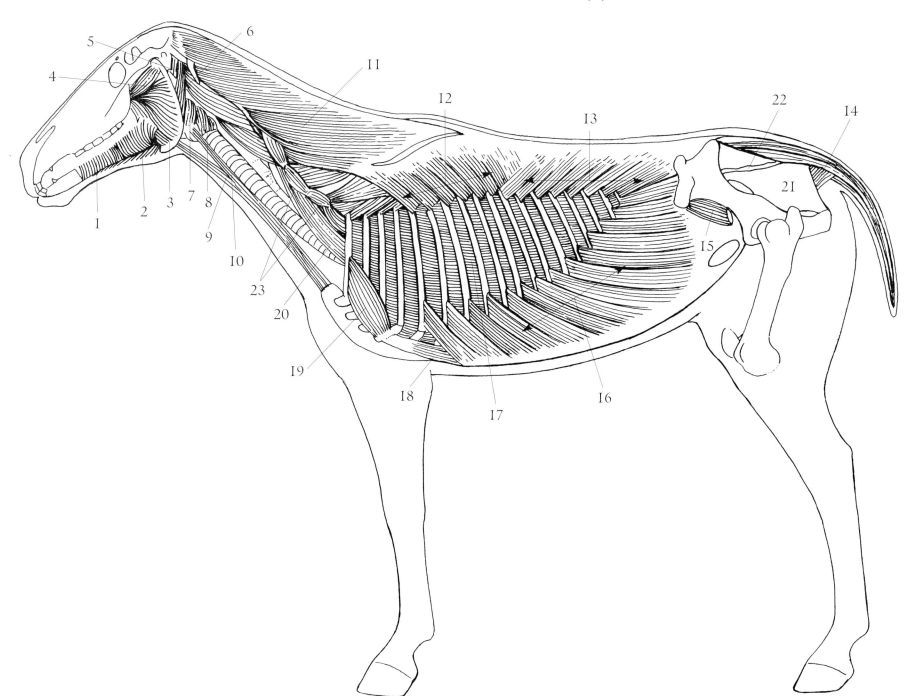

DEEP MUSCLES PART 4 –
Axial Musculature in Lateral View
(2) (Figure 28)

Identify and colour:

1. Geniohyoid muscle
2. Genioglossal muscle
3. Styloglossal muscle
4. Digastric muscle
5. Thyrohyoid muscle
6. Palatine muscles (tensor and levator)
7. Cranial and caudal capital oblique muscles
8. Capital spinal muscle
9. Atlantal longissimus muscle
10. Capital longissimus muscle
11. Longus capitis and longus calli muscles
12. Cervical longissimus muscle
13. Thoracic and cervical spinal muscle
14. Thoracic longissimus muscle
15. Lumbar longissimus muscle
16. Iliocostal muscle
17. Tail muscles (levators, lateral flexors and depressors)
18. Internal abdominal oblique muscle
19. Rectus abdominus muscle

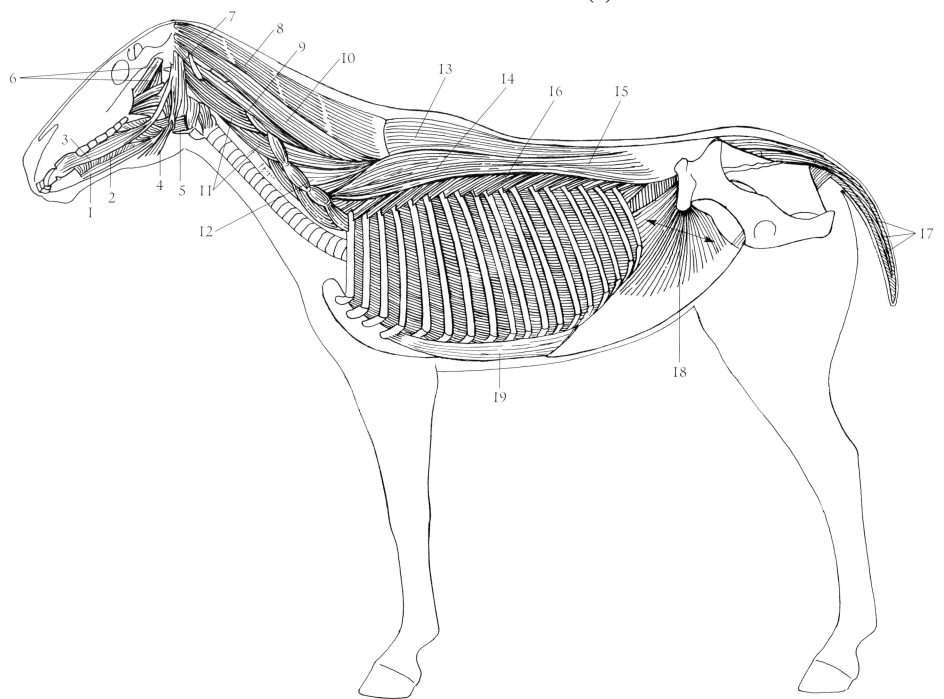

MUSCLES – Dorsal and Ventral Views (Figure 29)

Fig. 29(a) Superficial and Deep Muscles – Dorsal View

Label:

A   Lumbodorsal fascia

B   Gluteal fascia

Identify and colour:

1   Scutularis muscle

2   Auricular levator muscle

3   Auricular abductor muscle

4   Splenius muscle

5   Complexus muscle

6   Cervical part of ventral serrate muscle

7   Brachiocephalic muscle

8   Rhomboid muscle

9   Cervical part of trapezius muscle

10   Supraspinous muscle

11   Infraspinous muscle

12   Triceps muscle

13   Deltoid muscle

14   Thoracic part of trapezius muscle

15   Thoracic part of ventral serrate muscle

16   Spinalis dorsi

17   Latissimus dorsi muscle

18   External intercostal muscle

19   Longissimus dorsi muscle

20   Iliocostal muscle

21   Caudal part of dorsal serrate muscle

22   Costal retractor muscle

23   Transverse abdominal muscle

24   Internal abdominal oblique muscle

25   External abdominal oblique muscle

26   Medial gluteal muscle

27   Superficial gluteal muscle

28   Biceps femoris muscle

29   Semitendinosus muscle

30   Tail levator muscle

16   Semimembranosus muscle

17   Semitendinosus muscle

18   Adductor muscle

Fig. 29(b) Muscles – Ventral View

Identify and colour:

1   Omohyoid muscle

2   Sternohyoid muscle

3   Sternomandibular part of sternocephalic muscle

4   Brachiocephalic muscle

5   Cervical subcutaneous muscle

6   Cranial superficial pectoral muscle

7   Caudal superficial pectoral muscle

8   Caudal deep pectoral muscle

9   Ventral serrate muscle

10   External abdominal oblique muscle

11   Abdominal subcutaneous muscle

12   Femoral quadriceps muscle

13   Sartorius muscle

14   Iliopsoas muscle

15   Gracilis muscle

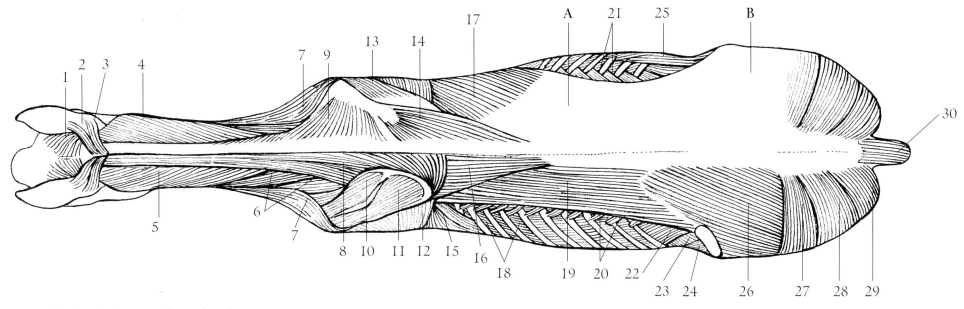

Fig. 29(a) Superficial and deep muscles – dorsal view

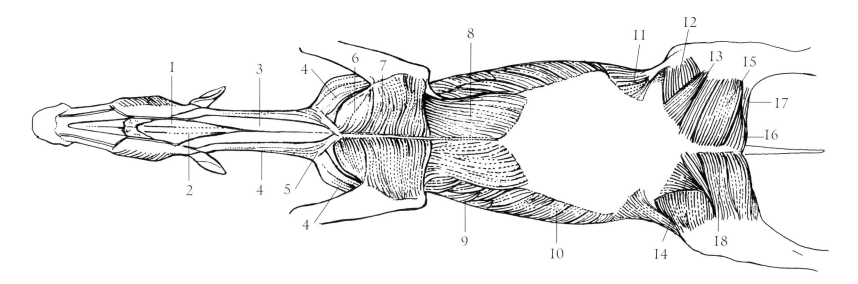

Fig. 29(b) Muscles – ventral view

MUSCLES – Cranial and Caudal Views (Figure 30)

Fig. 30(a) Cranial View

Identify and colour:

1. Interscutular muscle
2. Levator muscle of upper lip and nostril wing
3. Levator muscle of upper lip
4. Masseter muscle
5. Transverse nasal muscle
6. Sternothyrohyoid muscle
7. Sternomandibular part of sternocephalic muscle
8. Brachiocephalic muscle
9. Remains of skin muscle in neck (cutaneous colli)
10. Cranial superficial pectoral muscle
11. Cervical part of trapezius muscle
12. Cranial deep pectoral muscle
13. Supraspinatus muscle
14. Long head of triceps muscle
15. Lateral head of triceps muscle
16. Brachialis muscle
17. Caudal superficial pectoral muscle
18. Radial carpal extensor muscle
19. Oblique carpal extensor muscle and tendon

Fig. 30(b) Superficial Muscles – Caudal View

Identify and colour:

1. Levator muscle of tail
2. Superficial gluteal muscle
3. Biceps femoris muscle ⎫
4. Semitendinosus muscle ⎬ components of hamstring group of muscles
5. Semimembranosus muscle ⎭
6. Gracilis muscle
7. Gastrocnemius muscle
8. Soleus muscle
9. Deep digital flexor muscle
10. Lateral digital extensor muscle

FIGURE 30: MUSCLES – Cranial and Caudal Views

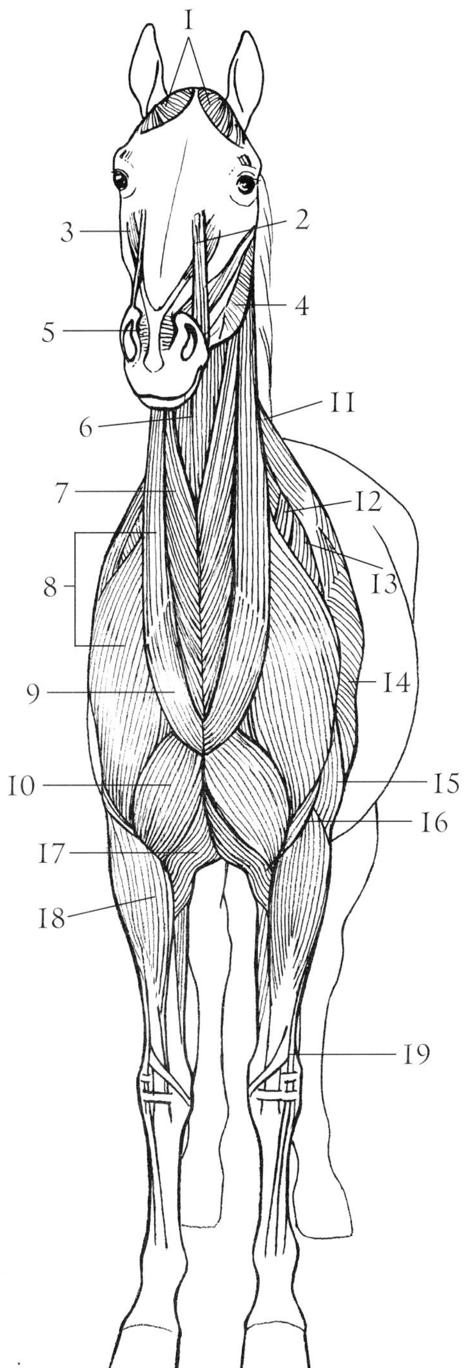

Fig. 30(a) Cranial view

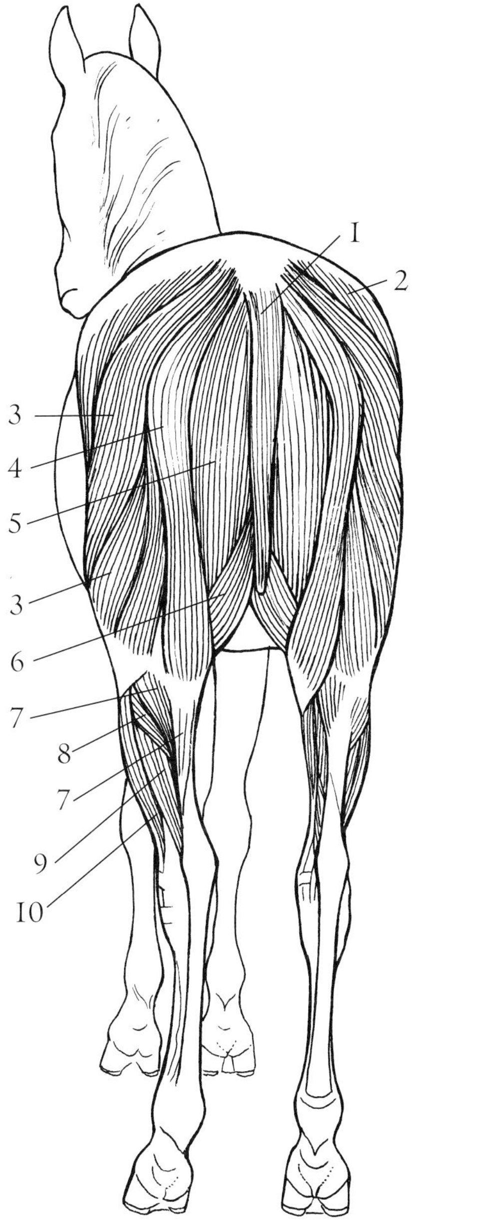

Fig. 30(b) Superficial muscles – caudal view

TENDONS AND TENDON SHEATHS OF THE FORELIMB – Lateral and Medial Views and Axial Section of Digit
(Figure 31)

Identify and colour the following, using the same colour for all parts of each structure, on all of the drawings on which each appears.

(1)   Radial carpal extensor muscle; (1a) tendon sheath; (1b) tendon

(2)   Common digital extensor muscle; (2a) tendon sheath; (2b) tendon

(3)   Lateral digital extensor muscle; (3a) tendon sheath; (3b) tendon

(4)   Deep digital flexor muscle; (4a) carpal synovial sheath (surrounding deep digital flexor tendon in carpal canal) ; (4b) tendon; (4c) subcarpal (inferior) check ligament (tendinous head of deep digital flexor muscle uniting deep flexor tendon with palmar carpal ligament); (4d) digital synovial sheath (surrounding deep and superficial flexor tendons)

(5)   Lateral ulnar muscle; (5a) tendon sheath; (5b) long tendon

(6)   Ulnar carpal flexor muscle; (6a) tendon

(7)   Radial carpal flexor muscle; (7a) tendon sheath; (7b) tendon

(8)   Tendon of superficial digital flexor muscle

(9)   Palmarolateral pouch of antebrachiocarpal joint capsule (between long tendon of lateral ulnar muscle and lateral styloid process of radius)

(10) Proximal extension of fetlock joint capsule (between cannon and suspensory ligament)

(11) Synovial bursa under common digital extensor tendon (where tendon crosses front of fetlock joint)

(12) Palmar annular ligament of fetlock joint

(13) Proximal digital annular ligament

(14) Suspensory band from 1st phalanx to lateral cartilage of 3rd phalanx (chondrocompedal ligament)

(15) Suspensory ligament of navicular bone (collateral sesamoidean ligament)

(16) Suspensory (superior sesamoidean) ligament

(17) Distal digital annular ligament

(18) Navicular synovial bursa

(19) Distal navicular ligament

(20) Fetlock joint capsule

(21) Pastern joint capsule

(22) Coffin joint capsule

(23) Distal (inferior) sesamoidean ligament

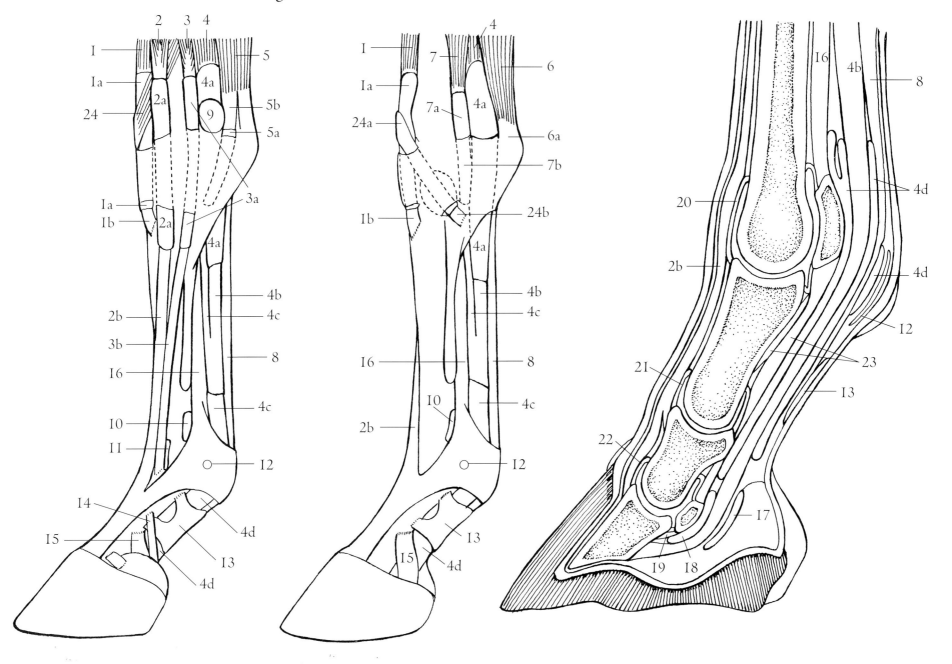

Fig. 31(a) Lateral view   Fig. 31(b) Medial view   Fig. 31(c) Axial section of digit

TENDONS AND TENDON SHEATHS OF THE HOCK – Lateral and Medial Views
(Figure 32)

Identify and colour the following, using the same colour for all parts of each structure, on one or both of the drawings as appropriate.

① Long digital extensor muscle; ①a tendon sheath; ①b tendon

② Lateral digital extensor muscle; ②a tendon sheath; ②b tendon

③ Deep digital flexor muscle (lateral head); ③a tendon sheath; ③b tendon; ③c tarsal synovial sheath

④ Deep digital flexor muscle (medial head); ④a tendon sheath

⑤ Achilles' tendon

⑥ Tendon of superficial digital flexor

⑦ Cranial tibial muscle; ⑦a tendon sheath; ⑦b medial tendon; ⑦c dorsal tendon

⑧ Tendon of peroneus tertius

⑨ Lateroplantar pouch

⑩ Medioplantar pouch

⑪ Dorsal pouch

⑫ Synovial bursa under median tendon of cranial tibial muscle

⑬ Suspensory ligament

⑭ Synovial bursa under superficial digital flexor tendon (where tendon crosses point of hock joint)

⑮ Common calcaneal tendon (aggregate of tendons attaching to calcaneal tuberosity, including Achilles' tendon and tarsal tendon of hamstring group)

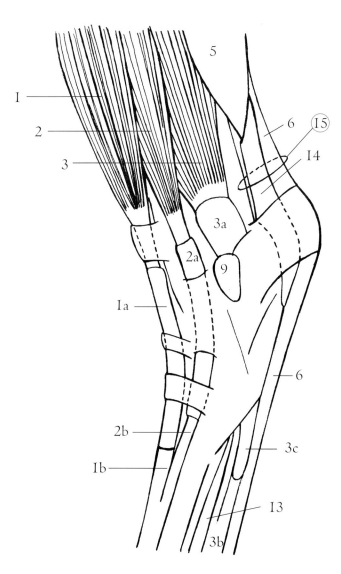

Fig. 32(a) Lateral view

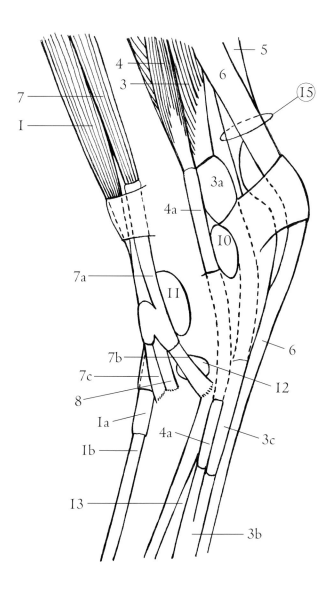

Fig. 32(b) Medial view

THE STAY APPARATUS –
Lateral View (Figure 33)

Identify the following and colour-match the numbered circles with those on the drawing (i.e. colour the numbered circles on the drawing the same as their correspnding number in the text).

(1) Cervical part of rhomboid muscle

(2) Cervical part of ventral serrate muscle

(3) Thoracic part of ventral serrate muscle

(4) Supraspinatus muscle

(5) Biceps brachii muscle

(6) Long head of triceps muscle

(7) Lateral head of triceps muscle

(8) Medial head of triceps muscle

(9) Lacertus fibrosus

(10) Radial carpal extensor muscle

(11) Conjoint tendon of radial carpal extensor muscle and lacertus fibrosus

(12) Superficial digital flexor muscle

(13) Tendon of superficial digital flexor muscle

(14) Radial check ligament

(15) Deep digital flexor muscle

(16) Tendon of deep digital flexor muscle

(17) Carpal check ligament

(18) Suspensory ligament

(19) Distal sesamoidean ligament

(20) Tendon of common digital extensor muscle

(21) Extensor branch of suspensory ligament attaching to common digital extensor tendon

(22) Gluteal muscles

(23) Tensor muscle of lateral fascia of thigh

(24) Rectus femoris muscle

(25) Vastus muscles

(26) Biceps femoris

(27) Semitendinosus muscle

(28) Accessory or tarsal tendon from the biceps femoris and semitendinosus muscles

(29) Straight patellar ligaments

(30) Peroneus tertius muscle

(31) Gastrocnemius muscle

(32) Tarsal check ligament

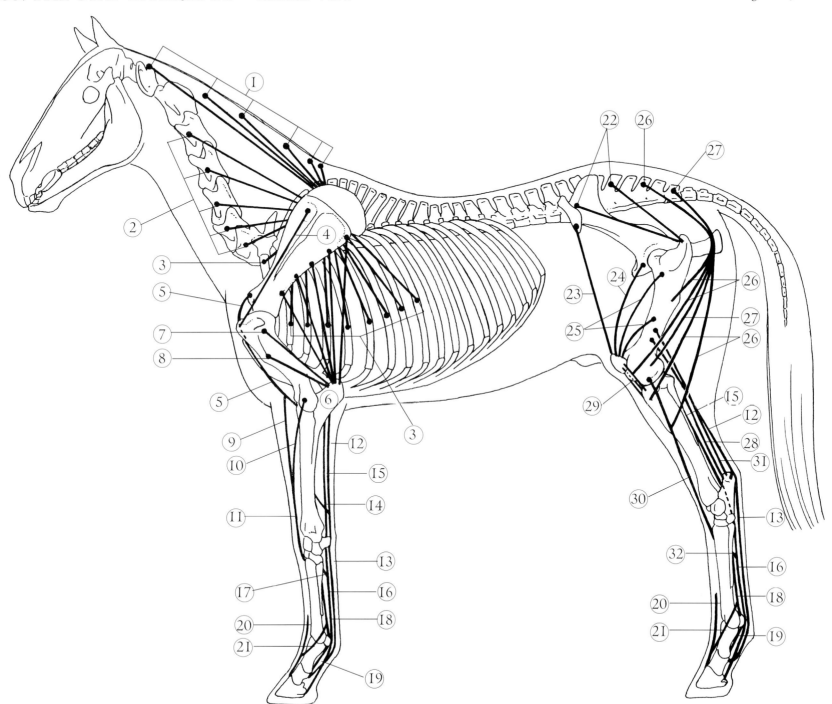

PART 4 — *Blood Vessels and Lymph Nodes*

MAJOR ARTERIES –
Lateral Overview (Figure 34)

Identify the following and colour-match the numbered circles with those on the drawing (i.e. colour the numbered circles on the drawing the same as their corresponding number in the text); colour each artery in red.

1. Maxillary and mandibular labial arteries
2. Dorsal and lateral nasal arteries
3. Buccal artery
4. Lingual and sublingual arteries
5. Infraorbital artery
6. Maxillary artery
7. Facial artery
8. Linguofacial artery
9. External carotid artery
10. Anastomosis between vertebral and occipital arteries
11. Cranial thyroid artery
12. Spinal arteries
13. Oesophageal and tracheal arteries
14. Left common carotid artery
15. Vertebral artery
16. Deep cervical artery
17. Dorsal scapular artery
18. Left subclavian artery
19. Superficial cervical artery
20. Axillary artery
21. Bicarotid artery
22. Subscapular artery
23. Deep brachial artery
24. Transverse cubital artery
25. Collateral ulnar artery
26. Cranial interosseus artery
27. Common interosseus artery
28. Median artery
29. Deep carpal branch from transverse cubital
30. Medial and lateral dorsal metacarpal arteries
31. Dorsal branches of palmar digital artery
32. Branch of palmar digital artery
33. Medial and lateral palmar digital artery
34. Medial and lateral palmar metacarpal arteries
35. Cranial epigastric artery
36. Musculophrenic artery
37. Bronchoesophageal artery
38. Aortic arch
39. Spinal arteries
40. Thoracic aorta
41. Abdominal aorta
42. Lumbar arteries
43. Dorsal intercostal arteries
44. Ventral intercostal arteries
45. Left gonadial artery
46. Deep circumflex iliac artery
47. External iliac artery
48. Internal iliac artery (dividing into caudal gluteal artery and internal pudendal artery)
49. Caudal epigastric and superficial epigastric arteries
50. Deep femoral artery
51. Sacral arteries
52. Descending genicular artery
53. Caudal arteries
54. Penile artery
55. Saphenous artery
56. Distal caudal femoral artery
57. Cranial saphenous artery
58. Caudal saphenous artery
59. Caudal tibial artery
60. Distal caudal femoral artery
61. Cranial tibial artery
62. Medial and lateral plantar arteries
63. Medial and lateral plantar metatarsal arteries
64. Dorsal metatarsal artery
65. Medial and lateral plantar digital arteries

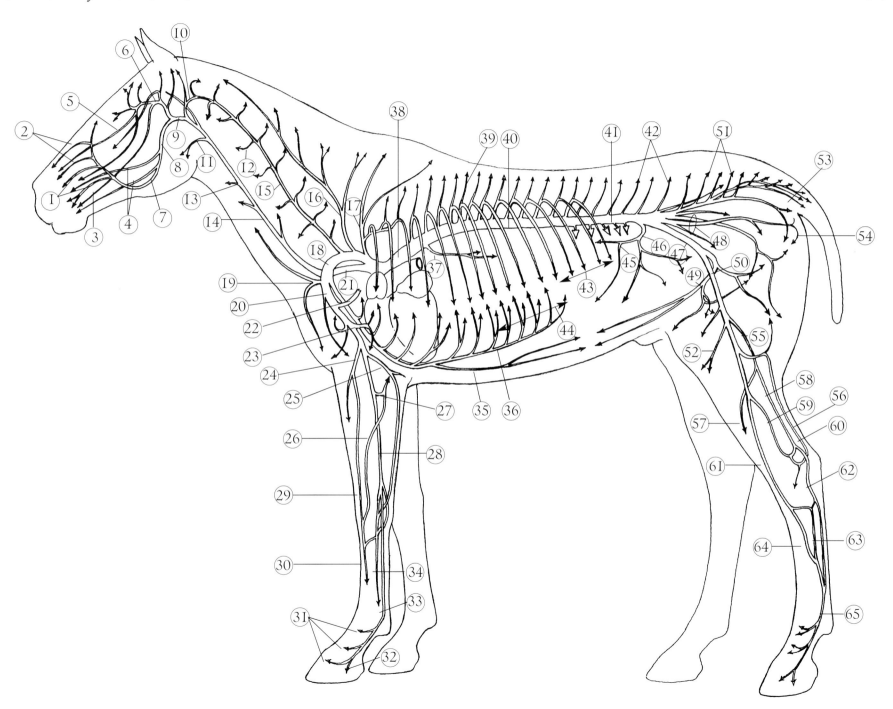

MAJOR VEINS – Lateral
Overview (Figure 35)

Identify the following and colour-match the numbered circles with those on the drawing; colour each vein in blue.

1. Linguofacial vein
2. Sinus of buccal vein
3. Sinus of deep facial vein
4. Sinus of transverse facial vein
5. Buccal vein
6. Lingual and sublingual veins
7. Inferior and superior labial veins
8. Dorsal and lateral nasal veins
9. Deep facial vein
10. Angularis oculi vein
11. Supraorbital vein
12. Transverse facial vein
13. Vertebral occipital vein anastomosis
14. Maxillary vein
15. External jugular vein
16. Inferior (mandibular) alveolar vein
17. Vertebral vein
18. Deep cervical vein
19. Dorsal scapular vein
20. Azygos vein
21. Internal thoracic vein
22. Costocervical vein
23. Cranial phrenic vein

24. Cephalic vein
25. Subclavian vein
26. Axillary vein
27. Subscapular vein
28. Transverse cubital vein
29. Cranial interosseus vein
30. Accessory cephalic vein
31. Medial and lateral palmar metacarpal veins
32. Dorsal common digital vein
33. Dorsal branches from 1st, 2nd and 3rd phalanges
34. Coronary venous plexus
35. Medial palmar vein
36. Median vein
37. Common interosseus vein
38. Collateral ulnar vein
39. Superficial thoracic vein
40. External thoracic vein
41. Musculophrenic vein
42. Ventral intercostal veins
43. Spinal branches of intercostal veins
44. Costoabdominal vein
45. Lumbar veins
46. Common iliac vein
47. Deep circumflex iliac vein
48. External iliac vein
49. Pudendoepigastric vein
50. Internal pudendal vein
51. Obturator vein
52. Caudal veins

53. Deep femoral vein
54. Penile veins
55. Femoral vein
56. Epigastric veins
57. Distal caudal femoral vein
58. Medial saphenous vein
59. Descending genual vein
60. Lateral saphenous vein
61. Caudal tibial vein
62. Caudal medial saphenous vein
63. Caudal tibial anastomoses with saphenous veins
64. Medial and lateral plantar veins
65. Perforating tarsal vein
66. Medial and lateral plantar metatarsal veins
67. Medial and lateral plantar digital veins
68. Dorsal metatarsal vein
69. Dorsal common digital vein
70. Dorsal pedal vein
71. Cranial medial saphenous vein

FIGURE 35: MAJOR VEINS – Lateral Overview

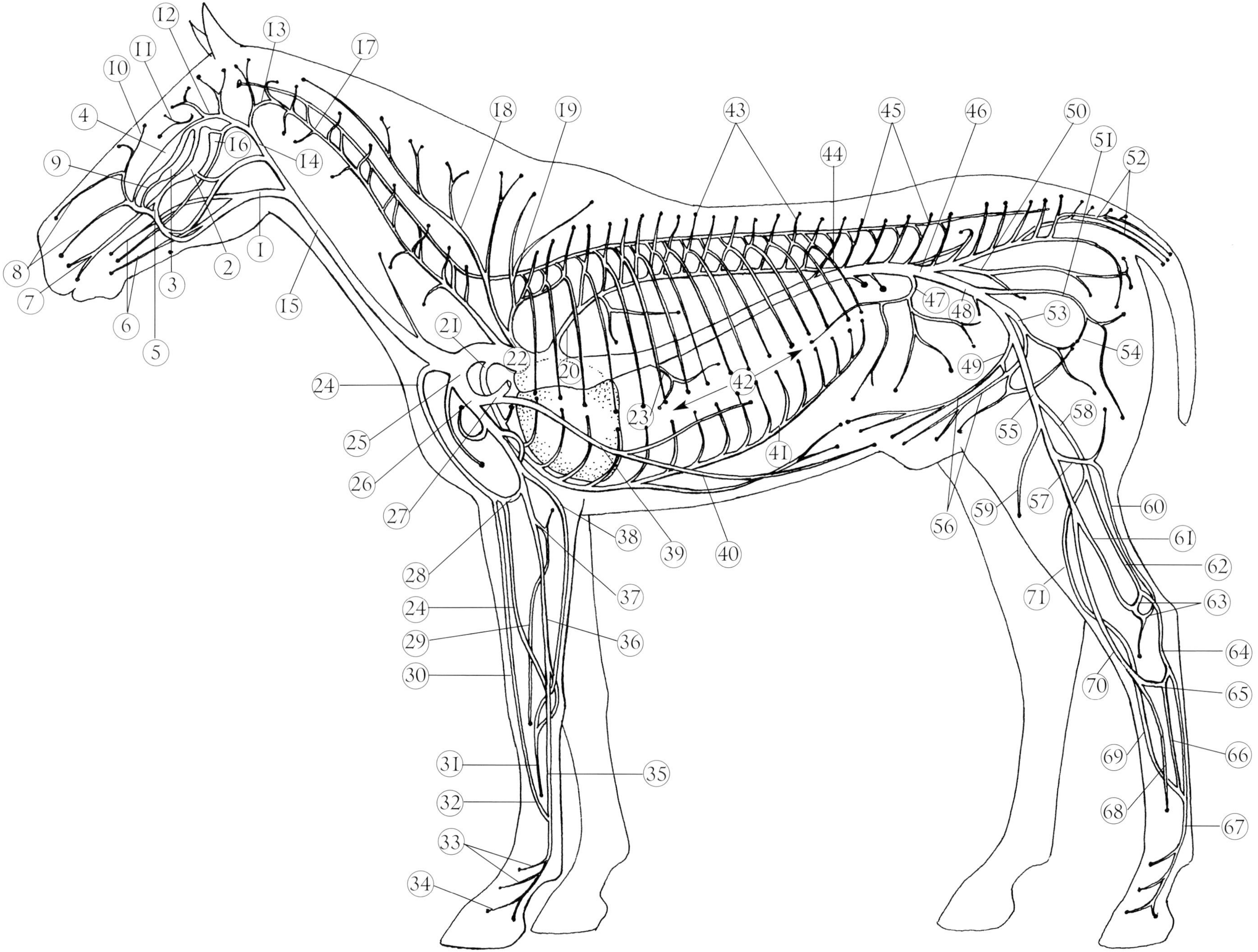

ARTERIES OF THE LOWER LIMBS – Cranial and Caudal Views of Fore and Hind
(Figure 36)

Figs. 36(a) and (b) Arteries of the Lower Forelimb

Identify and colour:

1. Cranial interosseous artery
2. Dorsal carpal branch from transverse cubital
3. Dorsal carpal branch of proximal radial artery
4. Medial and lateral dorsal metacarpal arteries
5. Dorsal branches of palmar digital arteries to 1st, 2nd and 3rd phalanges (on both drawings)
6. Proximal radial artery
7. Radial artery
8. Median artery
9. Deep palmar arch
10. Lateral palmar artery
11. Medial palmar artery
12. Medial and lateral palmar metacarpal arteries
13. Medial and lateral palmar digital arteries
14. Terminal arch (palmar digital arteries uniting inside 3rd phalanx)
15. Collateral ulnar artery

Figs. 36(c) and (d) Arteries of the Lower Hind Limb

Identify and colour:

1. Cranial tibial artery
2. Dorsal pedal artery
3. Dorsal metatarsal artery
4. Distal perforating artery (on both drawings)
5. Distal caudal femoral artery
6. Caudal tibial artery
7. Caudal saphenous artery
8. Medial and lateral plantar arteries
9. Medial and lateral plantar metatarsal arteries
10. Medial and lateral plantar digital arteries
11. Dorsal branches of plantar digital arteries to 1st, 2nd and 3rd phalanges
12. Terminal arch (plantar digital arteries uniting inside 3rd phalanx)

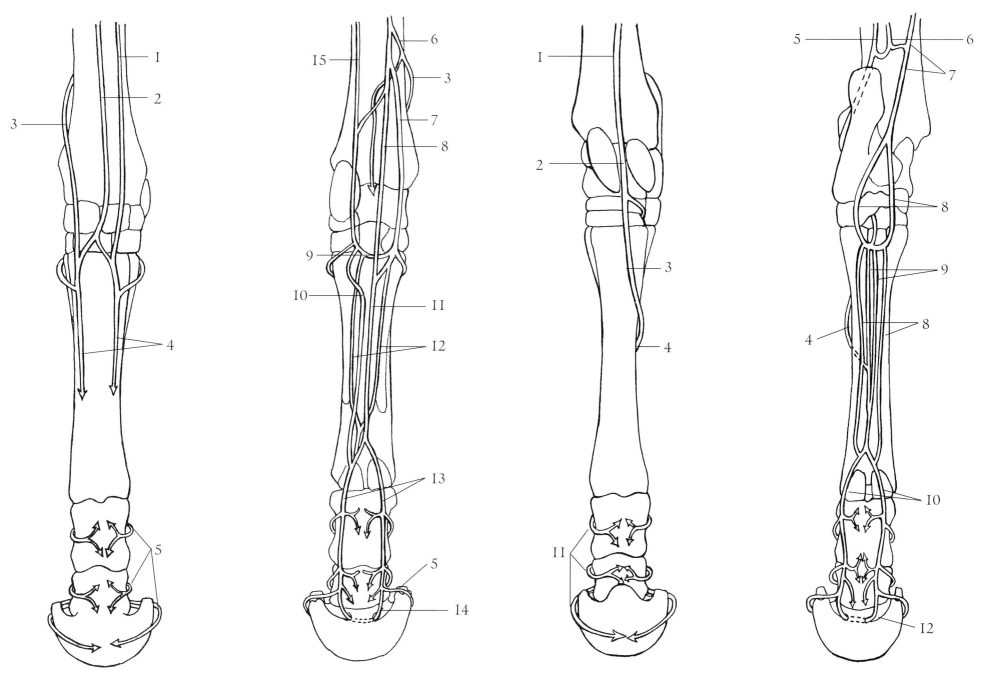

Fig. 36(a) Lower forelimb – cranial view   Fig. 36(b) Lower forelimb – caudal view   Fig. 36(c) Lower hind limb – cranial view   Fig. 36(d) Lower hind limb – caudal view

VEINS OF THE LOWER LIMBS – Cranial and Caudal Views of Fore and Hind
(Figure 37)

Figs. 37(a) and (b) Veins of the Lower Forelimb

Identify and colour the following on one or both of the drawings as appropriate.

1. Cranial interosseous vein
2. Accessory cephalic vein
3. Dorsal common digital vein
4. Dorsal branches of 1st, 2nd and 3rd phalanges
5. Coronary venous plexus
6. Collateral ulnar vein
7. Cephalic vein
8. Median vein
9. Radial vein
10. Deep palmar arch
11. Medial palmar vein (palmar common digital)
12. Lateral palmar vein
13. Medial and lateral palmar metacarpal veins
14. Medial and lateral palmar digital veins (palmar proper digitals)
15. Terminal arch

Figs. 37(c) and (d) Veins of the Lower Hind Limb

Identify and colour:

1. Cranial and medial saphenous veins
2. Cranial tibial vein
3. Dorsal pedal vein
4. Perforating tarsal vein
5. Dorsal metatarsal vein
6. Dorsal common digital vein
7. Caudal tibial vein
8. Caudal medial saphenous vein
9. Lateral saphenous vein
10. Medial and lateral plantar veins (plantar common digitals)
11. Medial and lateral plantar metatarsal veins
12. Distal perforating vein
13. Medial and lateral plantar digital veins
14. Dorsal branches of 1st, 2nd and 3rd phalanges
15. Coronary venous plexus
16. Terminal arch

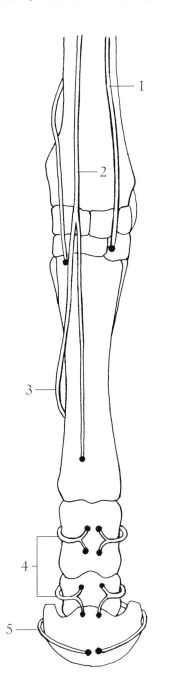

Fig. 37(a) Lower forelimb – cranial view

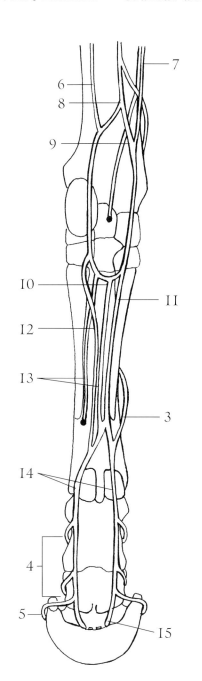

Fig. 37(b) Lower forelimb – caudal view

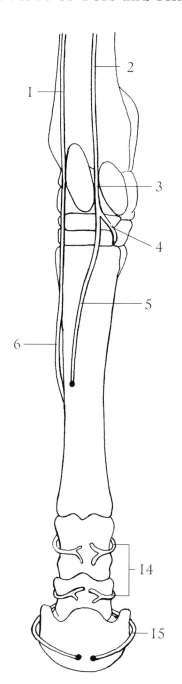

Fig. 37(c) Lower hind limb – cranial view

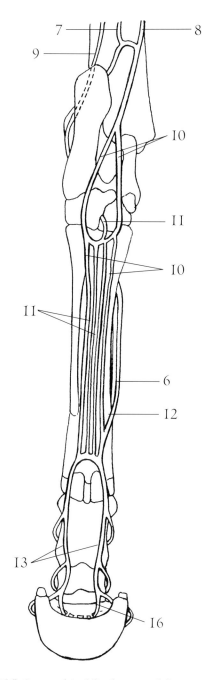

Fig. 37(d) Lower hind limb – caudal view

BLOOD VESSELS OF THE LOWER LIMBS – Lateral and Medial Views
(Figure 38)

These drawings also show the nerves of the lower limbs, which are identified in Figure 43.

Identify and colour-match the numbered circles with those on the drawings on which they appear – colour the arteries red and the veins blue.

1. Lateral palmar (plantar) vein
2. Lateral palmar (plantar) artery
3. Lateral palmar (plantar) digital vein
4. Lateral palmar (plantar) digital artery
5. Cephalic vein
6. Medial palmar (plantar) vein
7. Medial palmar (plantar) artery
8. Medial palmar (plantar) digital vein
9. Medial palmar (plantar) digital artery
10. Dorsal pedal artery
11. Dorsal pedal vein
12. Dorsal metatarsal vein
13. Caudal branch of lateral saphenous vein
14. Caudal femoral artery
15. Caudal tibial vein
16. Caudal tibial artery
17. Caudal branch of medial saphenous vein
18. Caudal saphenous artery
19. Dorsal common digital vein
20. Cranial branch of medial saphenous vein
21. Cranial saphenous artery
22. Coronary venous plexus

FIGURE 38: BLOOD VESSELS OF THE LOWER LIMBS – Lateral and Medial Views

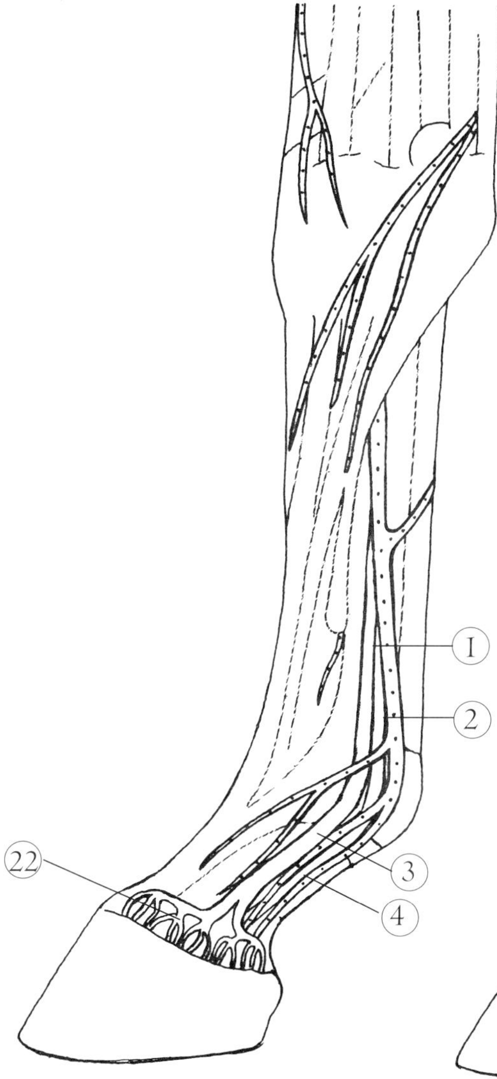

Fig. 38(a) Lower forelimb – lateral view

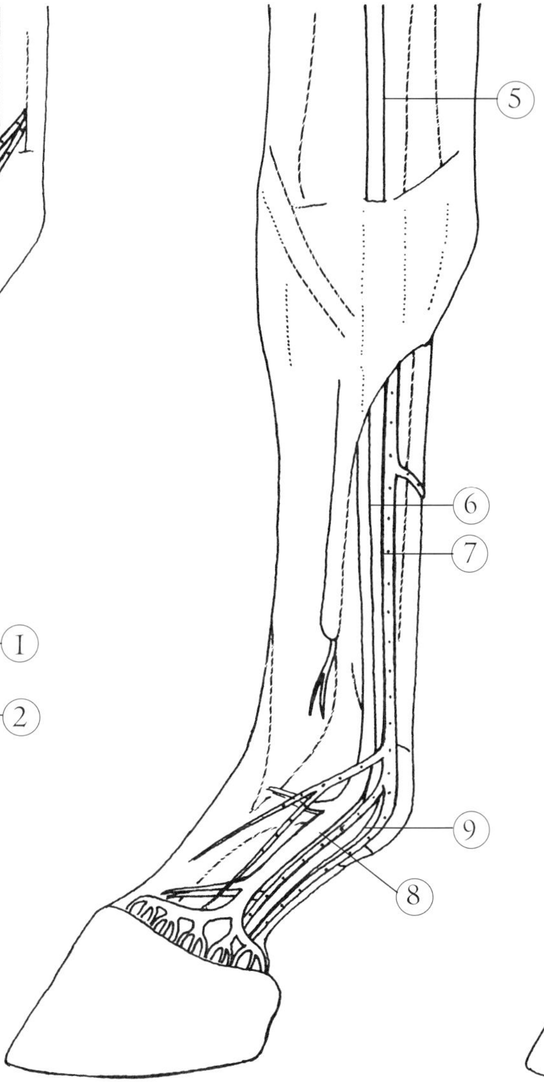

Fig. 38(b) Lower forelimb – medial view

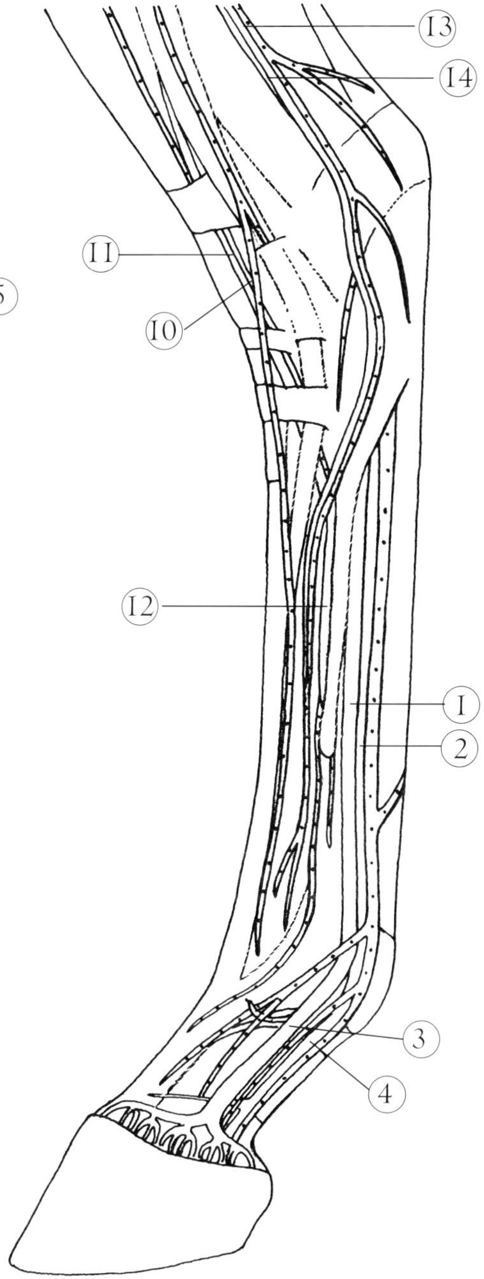

Fig. 38(c) Lower hind limb – lateral view

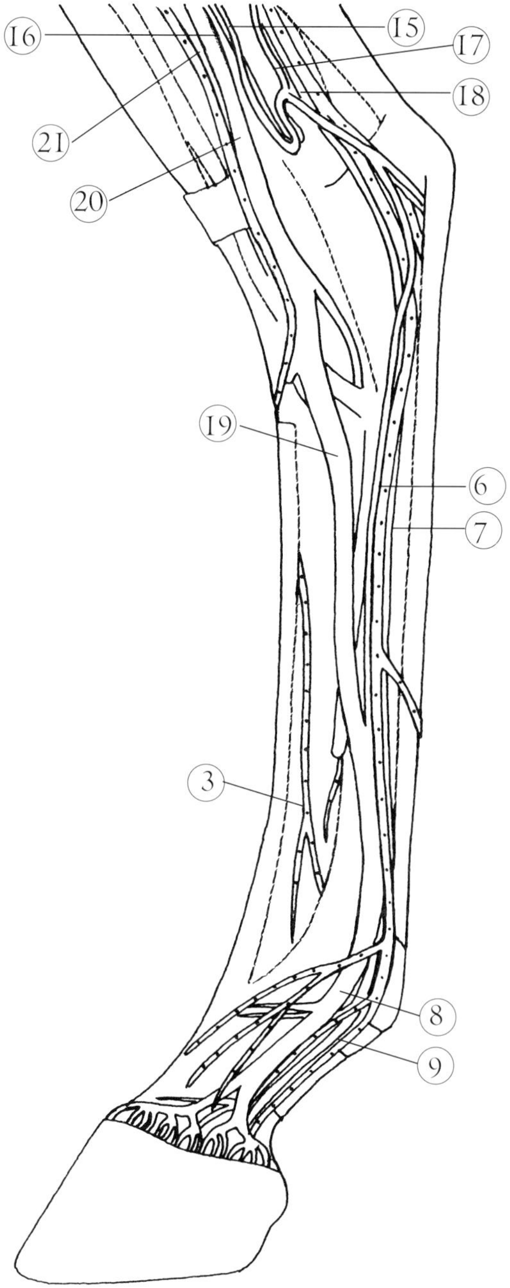

Fig. 38(d) Lower hind limb – medial view

MAJOR LYMPH NODE GROUPS – Lateral View (Figure 39)

Label the following major lymph nodes and ducts:

A Tracheal duct
B Lumbar lymph duct
C Cisterni chyli
D Thoracic duct

Identify the following and colour-match the numbered circles with those on the drawing.

① Mandibular nodes – lymph from skin of face; most of muscles and bones of head; nasal cavity, gums, teeth, tongue, hard palate and salivary glands

② Parotid nodes – lymph from skin of eyelids, cranial and parotid regions; jaw and eyeball muscles; lacrimal and parotid glands

③ Medial and ④ Lateral retropharyngeal nodes – lymph from bones, muscles, deep structures of head and cranial neck

⑤ Superficial cervical nodes – lymph from skin of ear, back of head, neck, shoulder, thorax and entire forelimb; jaw joint and bones and joints of forelimb (except ulna and elbow joint); muscles of shoulder and breast, digital flexor and extensor tendons

⑥ Cranial, ⑦ Middle, ⑧ Caudal deep cervical nodes

⑨ Axillary nodes – lymph from skin of shoulder, arm, thorax, cranial abdominal wall; shoulder and elbow joints and muscles of shoulder, arm and chest

⑩ Cubital nodes – lymph from skin, muscles, bones and joints of forelimb distal to node, elbow joint and brachiocephalic muscle

⑪ Intercostal nodes – lymph from muscles of back, upper thorax and abdominal wall; pleura, mediastinum and diaphragm

⑫ Thoracic aortic nodes – drainage as for intercostals, but also from liver

⑬ Cranial and ⑭ Caudal sternal nodes

⑮ Phrenic nodes – small, inconstant

⑯ Cranial, ⑰ Middle and ⑱ Caudal mediastinal nodes

⑲ Nuchal node – lymph from deep muscles of neck

⑳ Lumbar aortic nodes – lymph from muscles of back and loins; peritoneum and caudal pleura; urogenital organs and kidneys

㉑ Renal nodes – lymph from adrenal gland, kidney and ureter; peritoneum, liver and duodenum; testicle

㉒ Medial iliac nodes – lymph from muscles of loins, sacral region, thigh and hip joint; peritoneum and caudal pleura; urogenital organs

㉓ Sacral nodes – lymph from muscles of rump and thigh; vagina (in mare); seminal vesicles, prostate and bulbourethal glands (in stallion)

㉔ Lateral iliac nodes – lymph from abdominal muscles, kidney and diaphragm; peritoneum and caudal pleura

㉕ Obturator node – lymph from iliopsoas and cranial thigh muscles and hip joint

㉖ Anorectal nodes – lymph from skin and muscles of tail; rectum; anus; uterus, vagina, vulva and clitoris (in mares)

㉗ Superficial inguinal nodes – lymph from skin and muscles of caudal thoracic and abdominal wall; skin of hind limb; udder, vulva and clitoris (in mare); scrotum, prepuce and penis (in stallion)

㉘ Subiliac (prefemoral) nodes – lymph from skin of dorsal and lateral thorax and abdominal wall, lumbar and pelvic regions including thigh and stifle joint

㉙ Ischiatic nodes – lymph from tail, thigh muscles

㉚ Deep inguinal nodes – lymph from muscles of abdominal wall, cremaster muscle, all muscles of pelvis and thigh regions, muscles, tendons and joints of leg, foot, peritoneum and penis

㉛ Popliteal nodes

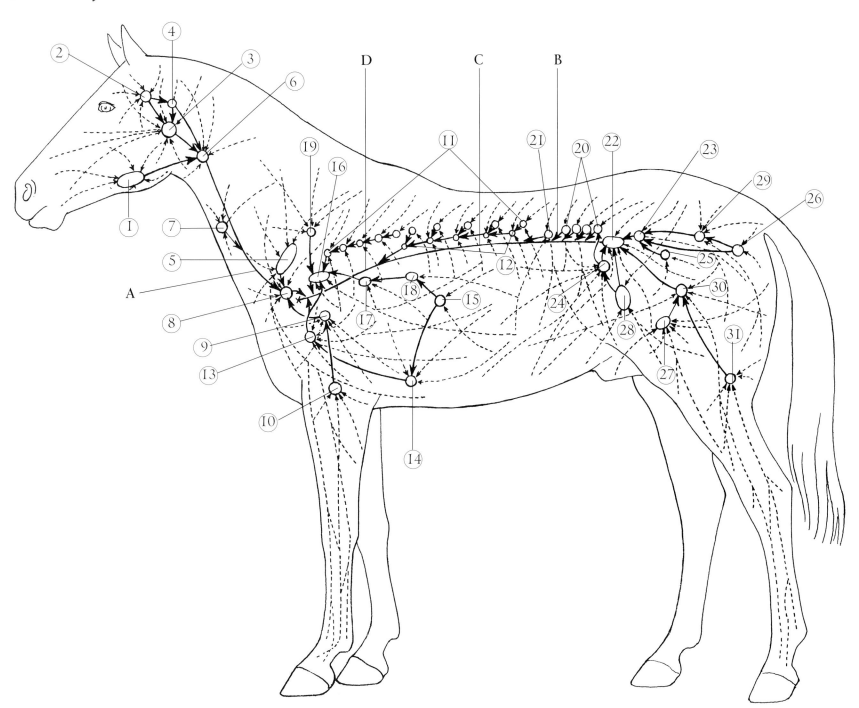

PART 5 – *The Nervous System*

THE BRAIN – Various Views
(Figure 40)

Figs. 40(a) Ventral View (Including Nerve Roots), (b) Dorsal View, (c) Lateral View and (d) Median Section

On Fig. (a), label the following cranial nerve roots:

- (I) Olfactory nerves
- (II) Optic nerve
- (III) Oculomotor nerve
- (IV) Trochlear nerve
- (V) Trigeminal nerve
- (VI) Abducent nerve
- (VII) Facial nerve
- (VIII) Vestibulocochlear nerve
- (IX) Glossopharyngeal nerve
- (X) Vagus nerve
- (XI) Accessory nerve
- (XII) Hypoglossal nerve

On Fig.(b), label:

- A Left cerebral hemisphere
- B Right cerebral hemisphere
- C Gyri (convultions)
- D Sulci (grooves)
- E Longitudinal fissure
- F Cerebellum

On all drawings on which they occur, identify and colour the following:

Forebrain

- (1) Spinal cord
- (2) Transverse cerebral fissure (separating cerebellum from cerebral hemisphere)
- (3) Frontal lobe
- (4) Parietal lobe
- (5) Occipital lobe
- (6) Temporal lobe
- (7) Olfactory lobe
- (8) Body of corpus callosum
- (9) Septum pellucidum
- (10) Olfactory tracts
- (11) Olfactory bulbs
- (12) Terminal lamina (thin rostral wall of brain stem in forebrain)
- (13) 3rd ventricle
- (14) Thalamus
- (15) Optic chiasma
- (16) Optic tract
- (17) Hypophysis (pituitary gland)
- (18) Mammillary body
- (19) Epiphysis

Midbrain

- (20) Cerebral crus
- (21) Tectum
- (22) Tegmentum

Hindbrain

- (23) Medulla oblongata
- (24) Pons
- (25) 4th ventricle
- (26) Cerebellar cortex
- (27) Cerebellar white matter

FIGURE 40: THE BRAIN – Various Views

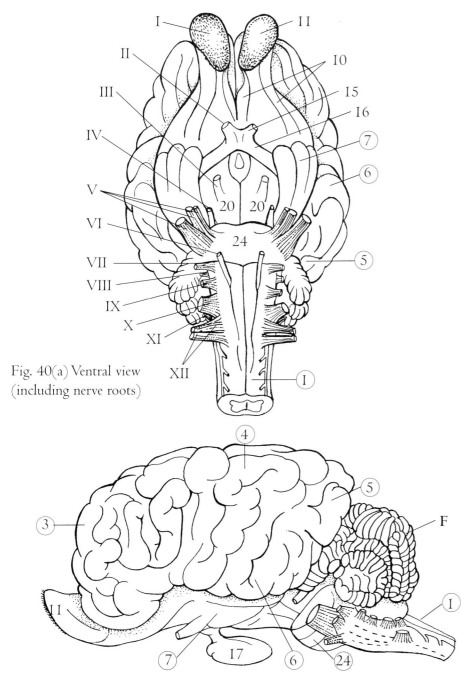

Fig. 40(a) Ventral view
(including nerve roots)

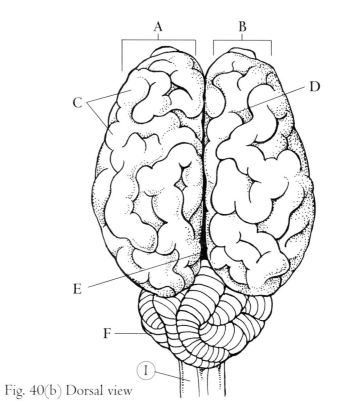

Fig. 40(b) Dorsal view

Fig. 40(c) Lateral view

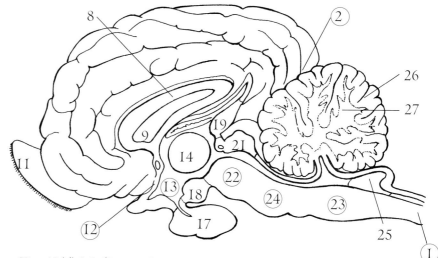

Fig. 40(d) Median section

PERIPHERAL NERVES –
Lateral Overview (Figure 41)

Identify the following and colour-match the numbered circles with those on the drawing. Where possible, fill in the nerves with one overall colour.

(1) Opthalmic component of trigeminal nerve

(2) Maxillary component of trigeminal nerve

(3) Mandibular component of trigeminal nerve

(4) Accessory nerve

(5) Suboccipital nerve

(6) Ventral rami of cervical nerves CI to C8

(7) Transverse cervical nerve

(8) Vagus nerve

(9) Ventral rami C3 to C5

(10) Ventral rami C6 to C8

(11) Phrenic nerve C5 to C7

(12) Suprascapular nerve

(13) Musculocutaneous nerve

(14) Axillary nerve

(15) Radial nerve

(16) Medial cutaneous antebrachial nerve

(17) Cranial cutaneous antebrachial nerve

(18) Lateral cutaneous antebrachial nerve

(19) Dorsal branch of ulnar nerve

(20) Medial and lateral dorsal metacarpal nerves

(21) Dorsal branch of palmar digital nerve

(22) Palmar branch of palmar digital nerve

(23) Medial and lateral palmar digital nerves

(24) Medial and lateral palmar metacarpal nerves

(25) Lateral palmar nerve

(26) Caudal cutaneous antebrachial nerve

(27) Ulnar nerve

(28) Median nerve

(29) Lateral thoracic nerve

(30) Ventral cutaneous nerves of thorax

(31) Lateral cutaneous nerves of thorax

(32) Thoracodorsal nerve

(33) Long thoracic nerve

(34) Intercostal nerves T2 to T17

(35) Dorsal rami C3 to C5

(36) Dorsal rami C6 to C8

(37) Dorsal rami of thoracic nerves TI to T18

(38) Dorsal rami of lumbar nerves LI to L6

(39) Dorsal rami of sacral nerves SI to S5

(40) Dorsal rami of caudal nerves Cd I to Cd5

(41) Dorsal cutaneous nerves

(42) Ilioinguinal nerve L2

(43) Genitofemoral nerve L3 and L4

(44) Obturator nerve

(45) Caudal cutaneous femoral nerve

(46) Dorsal penile (clitoridal) nerve

(47) Ischiatic nerve

(48) Lateral cutaneous sural nerve

(49) Common peroneal nerve

(50) Motor branches from ischiatic nerve

(51) Saphenous nerve

(52) Superficial peroneal nerve

(53) Deep peroneal nerve

(54) Caudal cutaneous sural nerve

(55) Tibial nerve

(56) Deep branch of lateral plantar nerve

(57) Lateral plantar nerve

(58) Medial and lateral dorsal metatarsal nerves

(59) Medial and lateral plantar metatarsal nerves

(60) Dorsal branch of plantar digital nerve

(61) Intermediate branch of plantar digital nerve

(62) Plantar branch of plantar digital nerve

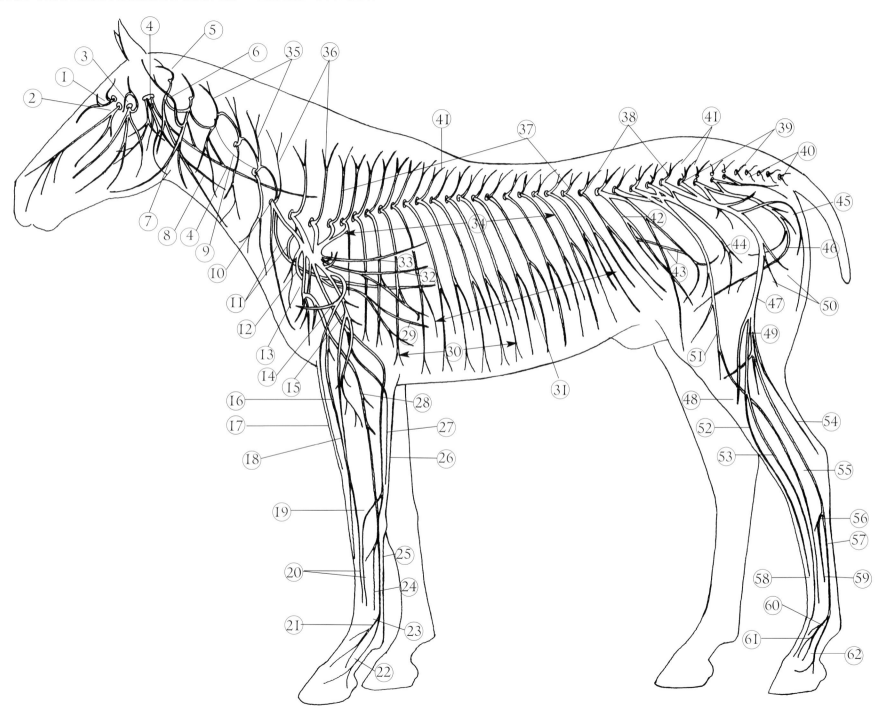

NERVES OF THE LOWER LIMBS – Cranial and Caudal Views (Figure 42)

Figs. 42(a) and (b) Lower Forelimb – Cranial and Caudal Views

Identify and colour the following on one or both drawings as appropriate.

1. Cranial cutaneous antebrachial nerve
2. Medial cutaneous antebrachial nerve
3. Lateral cutaneous antebrachial nerve
4. Dorsal branch of ulnar nerve
5. Medial and lateral dorsal metacarpal nerves
6. Dorsal branch of palmar digital nerve
7. Palmar branch of palmar digital nerve
8. Ulnar nerve
9. Median nerve
10. Palmar branch of ulnar nerve
11. Medial palmar nerve
12. Lateral palmar nerve
13. Deep branch of median and ulnar nerve
14. Medial and lateral palmar metacarpal nerves
15. Communicating branch between palmar nerves
16. Medial and lateral palmar digital nerves

Figs. 42(c) and (d) Lower Hind Limb – Cranial and Caudal Views

Identify and colour:

1. Saphenous nerve
2. Superficial peroneal nerve
3. Deep peroneal nerve
4. Medial and lateral dorsal metatarsal nerves
5. Medial and lateral dorsal digital nerves
6. Caudal cutaneous sural nerve
7. Tibial nerve
8. Medial plantar nerve
9. Deep branch of lateral plantar nerve
10. Lateral plantar nerve
11. Medial and lateral plantar metatarsal nerves
12. Communicating branch between medial and lateral plantar nerves
13. Medial and lateral plantar digital nerves
14. Dorsal branch of plantar digital nerve
15. Intermediate branch of plantar digital nerve
16. Plantar branch of plantar digital nerve (both drawings)

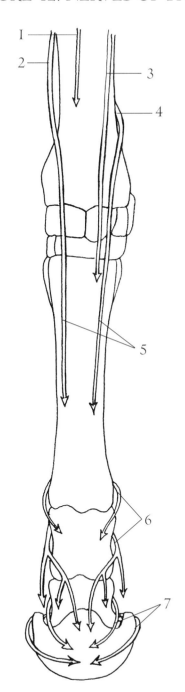

Fig. 42(a) Lower forelimb – cranial view

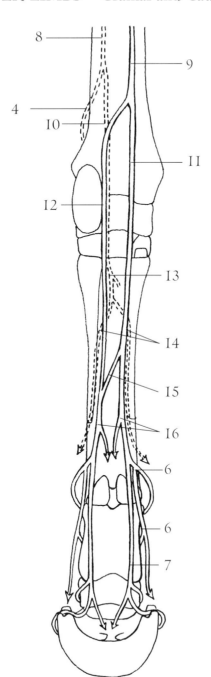

Fig. 42(b) Lower forelimb – caudal view

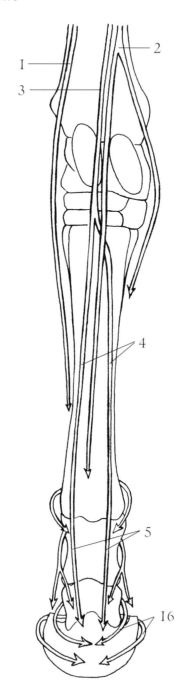

Fig. 42(c) Lower hind limb – cranial view

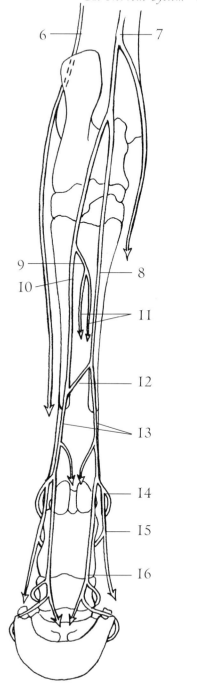

Fig. 42(d) Lower hind limb – caudal view

NERVES OF THE LOWER LIMBS – Lateral and Medial Views
(Figure 43)

These drawings also show the blood vessels of the lower limbs, which are identified in Figure 38.

On all drawings on which they occur, identify and colour the following.

1. Dorsal branch of the ulnar nerve
2. Lateral palmar (plantar) nerve
3. Communicating branch between palmar (plantar) nerves
4. Lateral palmar (plantar) digital nerve
5. Medial palmar (plantar) nerve
6. Medial palmar (plantar) digital nerve
7. Dorsal branch of palmar (plantar) digital nerve
8. Lateral plantar (caudal) cutaneous sural nerve
9. Palmar branch of palmar (plantar) digital nerve
10. Superficial peroneal nerve
11. Deep peroneal nerve
12. Tibial nerve
13. Saphenous nerve
14. Intermediate branch of palmar (plantar) digital nerve
15. Medial and lateral palmar metacarpal (plantar metatarsal) nerves
16. Medial and lateral dorsal metatarsal nerves

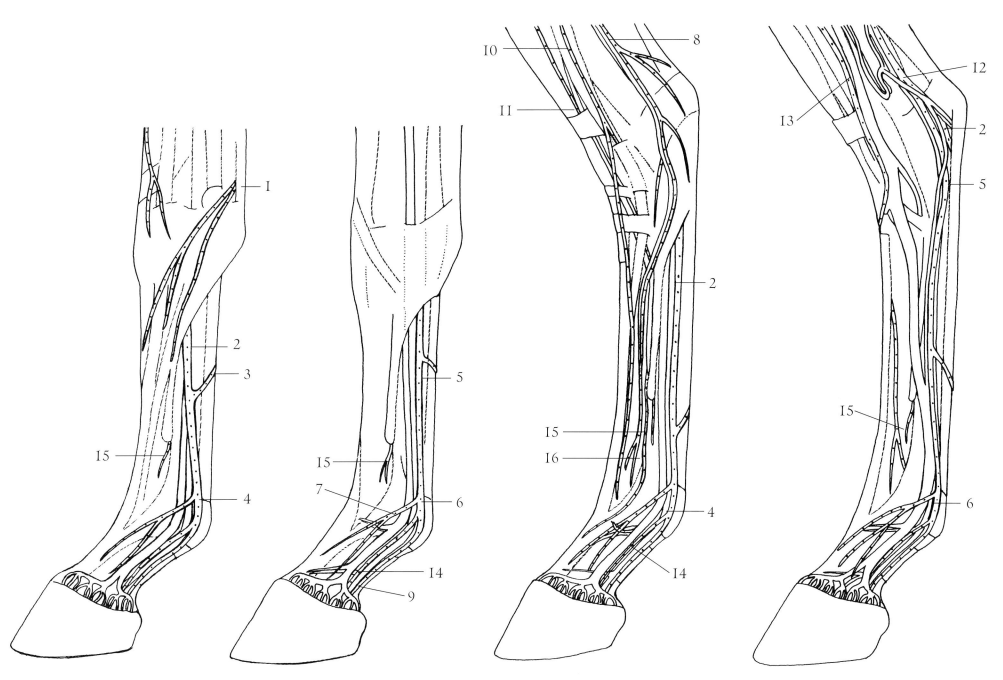

Fig. 43(a) Lower forelimb – lateral view Fig. 43(b) Lower forelimb – medial view Fig. 43(c) Lower hind limb – lateral view Fig. 43(d) Lower hind limb – medial view

PART 6 – *The Head*

SURFACE FEATURES AND SUBCUTANEOUS STRUCTURES OF THE HEAD – Lateral Views
(Figure 44)

Fig. 44(a) Surface Features

Identify and colour-match the numbered circles with those on the drawing.

1. External nostril (comma shaped)
2. Dorsal nasal commissure (false nostril leading into blind-ending nasal diverticulum)
3. Ventral nasal commissure (true nostril leading into nasal vestibule)
4. Medial nostril wing (supported by laminae of alar cartilage)
5. Lateral nostril wing (without cartilage support)
6. Upper lip
7. Lower lip
8. Prominence of chin
9. Body of mandible
10. Facial artery
11. Vascular groove of ventral mandibular border for passage of facial artery and vein and parotid duct: used as a pulse point
12. Facial nerve
13. Upper eyelid
14. Lower eyelid
15. Medial angle (canthus) of eye
16. Lateral angle (canthus) of eye
17. Pinna (visible part of external ear)
18. Facial crest (attachment for masseter muscle)
19. Wing of atlas
20. Parotid salivary gland

Fig. 44(b) Subcutaneous Structures

Identify and colour:

1. Nostril
2. Transverse nasal muscle
3. Levator muscle of upper lip
4. Dorsal part of lateral nasal muscle
5. Nasolabial levator muscle
6. Canine muscle
7. Sphincter muscle of mouth
8. Buccinator muscle
9. Retractor muscle of angle of mouth
10. Depressor muscle of lower lip
11. Facial artery and vein
12. Ventral buccal nerve
13. Masseter muscle
14. Massetric artery and vein
15. Tendon of sternomandibular
16. Sternohyoid and omohyoid muscle
17. Depressor muscle of lower eyelid
18. Sphincter muscle of palpebral fissure
19. Levator muscle of medial angle of eye
20. Frontoscutular muscle
21. Interscutular muscle
22. Scutiform cartilage
23. Parotidauricular muscle
24. Cervicoauricular muscle
25. Greater auricular nerve
26. Parotid salivary gland
27. Splenius muscle
28. Cutaneous colli nerve
29. Brachiocephalic muscle
30. External jugular vein
31. Sternomandibular muscle

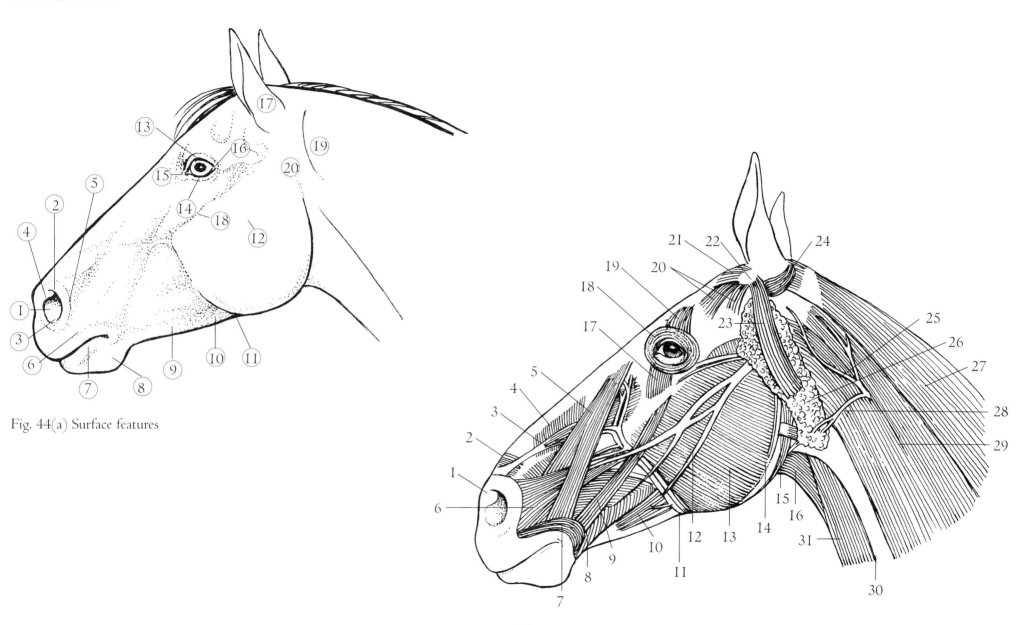

Fig. 44(a) Surface features

Fig. 44(b) Subcutaneous structures

DEEP STRUCTURES AND CAVITIES IN THE HEAD – Median Sections (Figure 45)

On both drawings as appropriate, label:

A   Dorsal nasal meatus

B   Middle nasal meatus

C   Ventral nasal meatus

D   Internal nostrils (exit from nasal cavity)

E   Laryngopharynx

F   Foramen magnum

G   Ethmoid conchae

H   Nasopharynx

I   Guttural pouch

On both drawings as appropriate, identify and colour the following.

(1)   Dorsal nasal concha

(2)   Ventral nasal concha

(3)   Frontal sinus

(4)   Cranial cavity

(5)   Sphenopalatine sinus

(6)   Hard palate

(7)   Ceratohyoid bone

(8)   Thyrohyoid bone

(9)   Stylohyoid bone

(10)   Epiglottic cartilage

(11)   Arytenoid cartilage

(12)   Thyroid cartilage

(13)   Lingual process

(14)   Soft palate

(15)   Pharyngeal opening of auditory tube

(16)   Opening into lateral laryngeal ventricle

(17)   Oesophagus

(18)   Trachea

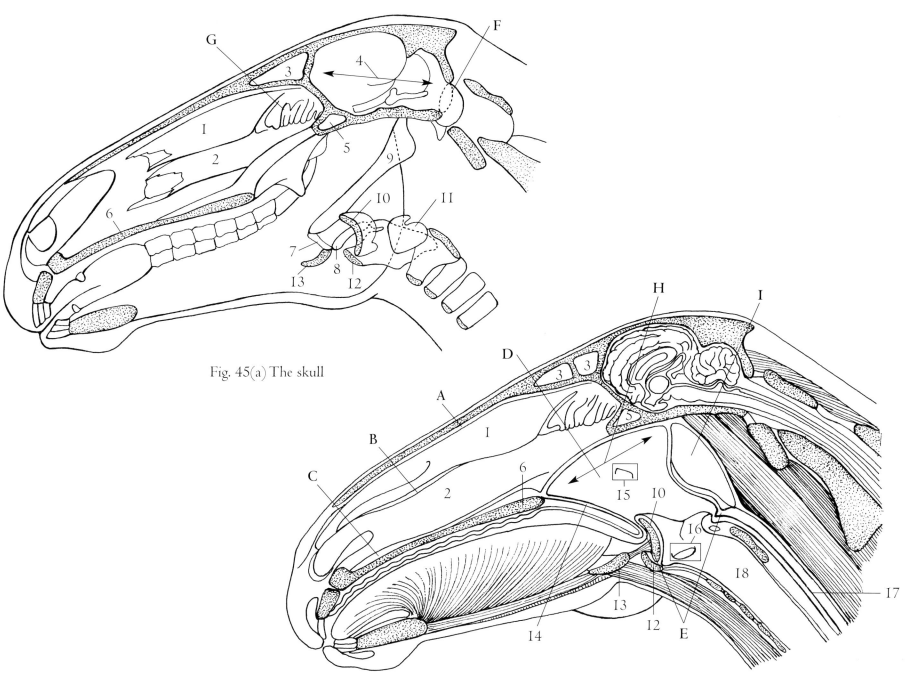

Fig. 45(a) The skull

Fig. 45(b) The head

NASAL AND ORAL CAVITIES –
Various Views (Figure 46)

(The small drawings show the orientation of the main drawings.)

On all drawings on which they occur, label the following.

A　Infraorbital canal

B　Nasolacrimal duct

C　Internal nostril

D　Tongue

E　Frontomaxillary opening

On all drawings on which they occur, identify and colour the following.

1　Cranial cavity

2　Nasal cavity

3　Caudal part of maxillary sinus

4　Rostral part of maxillary sinus

5　Nasopharynx

6　Laryngeal and tracheal cavities

7　Oral cavity

8　Oropharynx

9　Soft palate

10　Hard palate

11　Auditory (Eustachian) tube

12　Middle ear cavity

13　Maxillary foramen

14　Infraorbital foramen

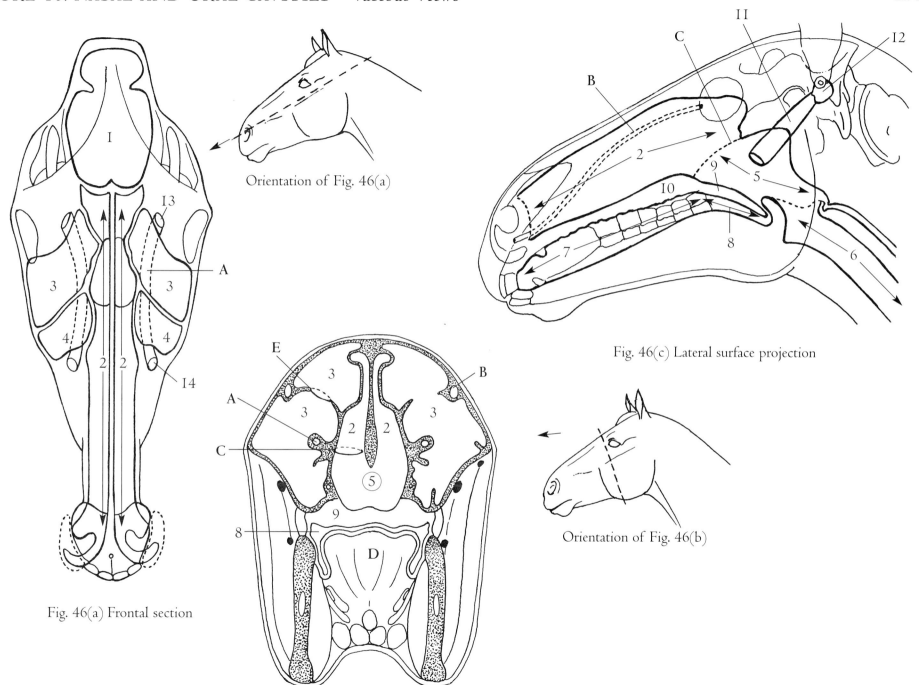

Orientation of Fig. 46(a)

Fig. 46(a) Frontal section

Fig. 46(c) Lateral surface projection

Orientation of Fig. 46(b)

Fig. 46(b) Nasal cavity and oropharynx – transverse section

PARANASAL SINUSES –
Various Views (Figure 47)

Fig. 47(a) and (b) Frontal and Maxillary Sinuses – Dorsal and Lateral Views and (c) Interconnections of Paranasal Sinuses – Lateral View

Label:

A   Frontal sinus

B   Maxillary sinus

C   Ventral conchal sinus

D   Dorsal conchal sinus

E   Sphenoid sinus

F   Palatine sinus

On all drawings on which they occur, identify and colour the following.

①   Frontal sinus (conchofrontal sinus since continues into dorsal conchal sinus)

②   Caudal maxillary sinus

③   Rostral maxillary sinus

④   Ventral conchal sinus (communicates with medial compartment of rostral maxillary sinus)

⑤   Dorsal conchal sinus

⑥   Sphenoid sinus

⑦   Palatine sinus

⑧   Frontomaxillary sinus

⑨   Frontomaxillary opening

⑩   Opening of sphenopalatine sinus into caudal maxillary sinus

⑪   Nasomaxillary opening

Colour in the path taken by the air travelling through the sinuses.

Fig. 47(d) Axes of Maxillary Sinuses – Lateral Surface View

To show how the approximate extent of the sinuses can be mapped from the surface using certain axes. Identify and label the following axes:

A—A   joining the rostral end of the facial crest to the infraorbital foramen

B—B   parallel to A—A and through the medial angle of the eye

C—C   from the nasoincisive notch back through the medial angle of the eye

D—D   along the length of the facial crest

Identify and colour:

①   Maxillary sinus

Fig. 47(e) Axes of Frontal Sinuses – Dorsal Surface View

To show how the approximate extent of the sinuses can be mapped from the surface using certain axes. Identify and label the following axes:

X—X   transversely through the middle of the zygomatic arches

Y—Y   transversely midway between the medial angle of the eye and the end of the facial crest

Z—Z   obliquely longitudinally from the nasomaxillary notch back through the medial angle of the eye

Identify and colour:

①   Frontal sinus

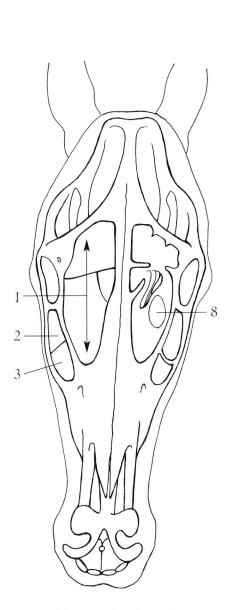

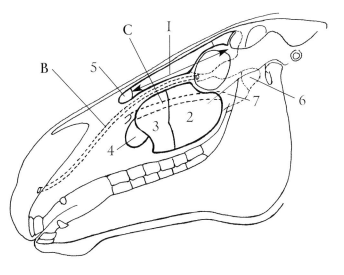

Fig. 47(b) Frontal and maxillary
sinuses – lateral view

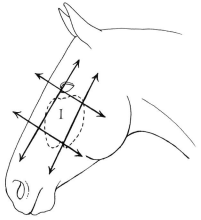

Fig. 47(d) Axes of maxillary sinuses –
lateral surface view

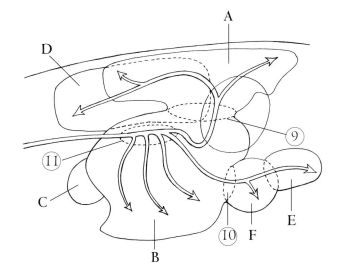

Fig. 47(c) Interconnections of paranasal sinuses – lateral view

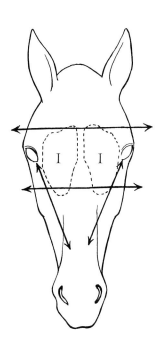

Fig. 47(e) Axes of frontal
sinuses – dorsal surface view

Fig. 47(a) Frontal and maxillary
sinuses – dorsal view

PHARYNX AND GUTTERAL POUCHES (Figure 48)

Fig. 48(a) Nasal Cavity, Pharynx and Larynx – Surface Projection

Identify and colour:

① Nasal cavity

② Nasopharynx

③ Soft palate

④ Auditory tube

⑤ Middle ear cavity

⑥ Oropharynx

⑦ Oesophagus

⑧ External acoustic meatus (across which eardrum is stretched)

Fig. 48(b) Guttural Pouch and Auditory Tube – Lateral Surface Projection

Label:

A   Auditory tube

B   Pharyngeal opening of auditory tube

C   Position of guttural pouch opening into auditory tube

D   Median septum of guttural pouches

E   Stylohyoid bone

F   Ceratohyoid

G   Basihyoid (body of hyoid)

H   Thyrohyoid

I   Epiglottic cartilage

J   Thyroid cartilage

Identify and colour:

① Guttural pouch

Fig. 48(c) Guttural Pouches – Ventral View

Identify and colour:

① Right guttural pouch (with ventral wall removed)

② Left guttural pouch

③ Vagosympathetic nerve

④ Common carotid artery

⑤ Cranial laryngeal nerve

⑥ Medial retropharangeal lymph node

⑦ Opening of auditory tube

⑧ Lateral compartment of guttural pouch

⑨ Stylohyoid bone

⑩ Internal carotid artery

⑪ External carotid artery

⑫ Hypoglossal nerve

⑬ Lingual artery

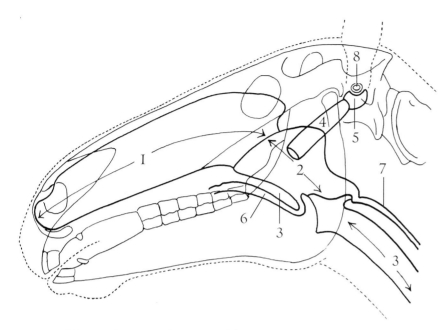

Fig. 48(a) Nasal cavity, pharynx and larynx – surface projection

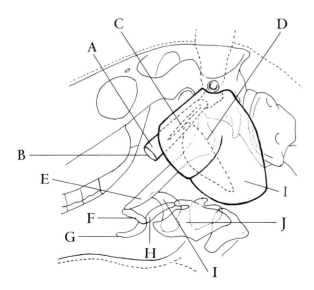

Fig. 48(b) Guttural pouch and auditory tube – lateral surface projection

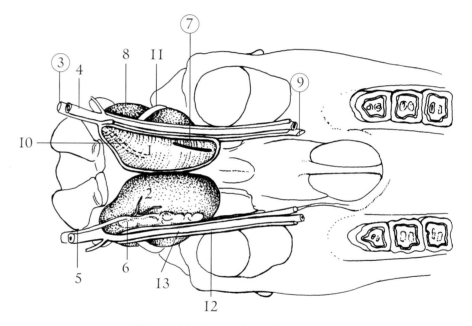

Fig. 48(c) Guttural pouches – ventral view

THE LARYNX PART I –
Breathing and Swallowing
(Figure 49)

Figs. 49(a), (b) Larynx and Glottis Open for Breathing and (c), (d) Larynx and Glottis Closed for Swallowing

Label:

A   Infraglottic cavity

B   Trachea

C   Oesophagus

D   Nasopharynx

E   Guttural pouch

Identify and colour:

1. Epiglottic cartilage

2. Soft palate

3. Oropharynx

4. Basihyoid bone

5. Laryngeal prominence of thyroid

6. Intrapharyngeal opening

7. Hyoepiglottic joint (hyoepiglottic ligament)

8. Root of tongue

9. Genioglossal muscle

10. Corniculate process of arytenoid cartilage (dorsal)

11. Vocal fold ('true' vocal fold covering vocal ligament and muscle)

12. Vestibular fold ('false' vocal fold covering vestibular ligament, ventricular muscle and cuneiform cartilage)

13. Pharyngeal constrictor muscles

14. Sternohyoid muscle

15. Geniohyoid muscle

16. Hyoglossal muscle

17. Arytenoid cartilage (hyaline with elastic processes)

18. Glottis

19. Median laryngeal ventricle

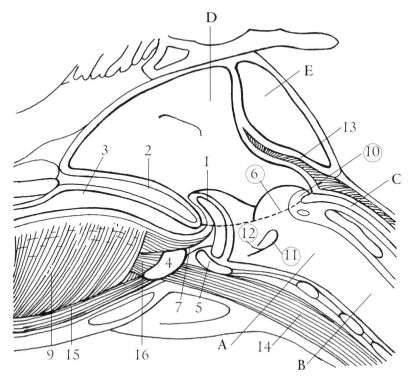

Fig. 49(a) Larynx open for breathing – median section

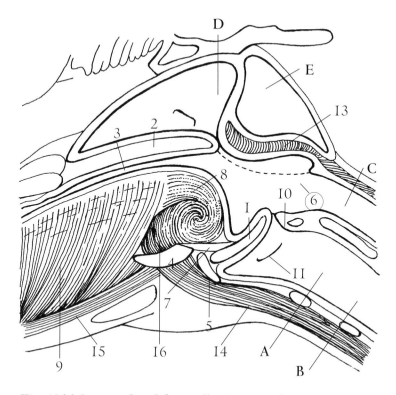

Fig. 49(c) Larynx closed for swallowing – median section

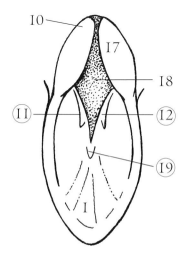

Fig. 49(b) Larynx with glottis open – rostral view

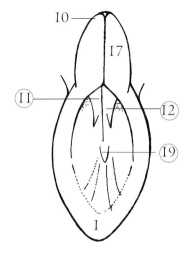

Fig. 49(d) Larynx with glottis closed – rostral view

THE LARYNX PART 2 – Hyoid Apparatus and Lateral Cartilages (Figure 50)

On all of the drawings on which they appear, label the following:

A   Rostral horn of thyroid cartilage

B   Corniculate process of arytenoid cartilage

C   Cuneiform process of epiglottic cartilage

D   Thyroid fissure (transmitting cranial laryngeal nerve)

E   Laryngeal prominence of thyroid

F   Entrance into laryngeal ventricle

G   Vocal fold

H   Trachea

I   Apex of epiglottis

J   Vestibular fold

On all of the drawings on which they appear, identify and colour the following.

(1)   Stylohyoid bone

(2)   Ceratohyoid bone

(3)   Lingual process of basihyoid in root of tongue

(4)   Thyrohyoid bone

(5)   Epiglottic cartilage (elastic)

(6)   Lamina of thyroid cartilage

(7)   Arytenoid cartilage

(8)   Lamina of cricoid cartilage

(9)   Tracheal cartilage

(10)   Dorsal cricoarytenoid muscle (glottic dilator abducting vocal folds to open glottis)

(11)   Cricothyroid muscle (glottic sphincter tensing and adducting vocal folds)

(12)   Thyrohyoid muscle

(13)   Ceratohyoid muscle

(14)   Transverse arytenoid muscle (glottic sphincter adducting vocal cords to close glottis)

(15)   Ventricular muscle (associated with vestibular ligament in vestibular fold: glottic sphincter adducting vestibular folds to close glottis)

(16)   Vocal muscle (associated with vocal ligament in vocal fold, forming a glottic sphincter adducting vocal folds to close glottis)

(17)   Cricotracheal ligament (annular band of fibro-elastic tissue)

(18)   Lateral laryngeal ventricle

(19)   Cricothyroid membrane (closing caudal notch of thyroid)

(20)   Hyoepiglottic joint (hyoepiglottic ligament)

(21)   Vestibular ligament

(22)   Thyrohyoid membrane

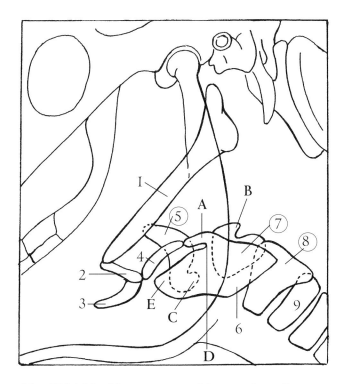

Fig. 50(a) Hyoid apparatus and laryngeal cartilages – lateral surface projection

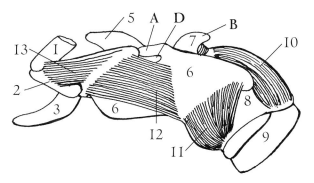

Fig. 50(b) Laryngeal cartilages and muscles – lateral view 1

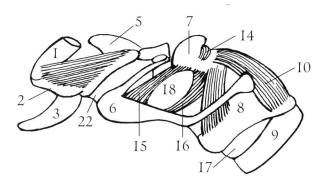

Fig. 50(c) Laryngeal cartilages and muscles – lateral view 2

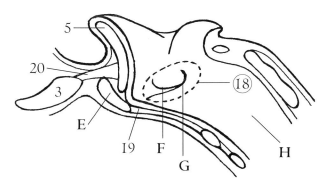

Fig. 50(d) Larynx in median section

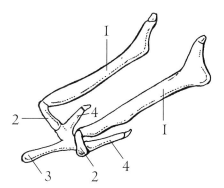

Fig. 50(e) Hyoid apparatus

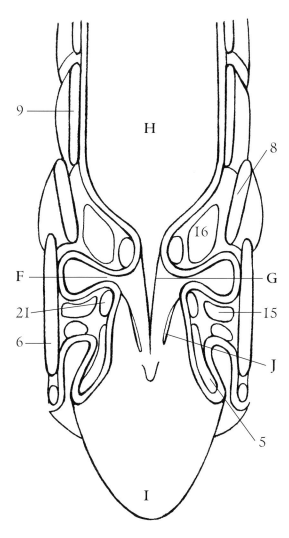

Fig. 50(f) Larynx in horizontal section – dorsal view

THE TONGUE AND SALIVARY GLANDS (Figure 51)

Fig. 51(a) Tongue, Palate and Larynx – Dorsal View

Label:

A   Apex of tongue (free and spatula-shaped)

B   Body of tongue (related below to mylohyoid and geniohyoid muscles)

C   Root of tongue (attached to hyoid and merging on either side with oropharyngeal wall)

D   Oropharynx (opened)

E   Oesophagus

F   Oral vestibule

Identify and colour:

1   Stylohyoid bone

2   Nasopharynx (roof cut in midline and pulled to one side)

3   Palatopharyngeal arch (caudal pillar of soft palate)

4   Corniculate process of arytenoid cartilage (mucosal covering dotted with lymph nodules)

5   Glottis (bounded by vocal cords and mucous membrane covering arytenoid cartilages)

6   Vocal fold

7   Aryepiglottic fold

8   Soft palate (oropharyngeal roof cut through in midline)

9   Lingual tonsil

10   Vallate papillae

11   Foliate papillae

12   Epiglottis

Fig. 51(b) Salivary Glands – Lateral Surface Projection

Label:

A   Opening of parotid duct (into oral vestibule through cheek lateral to upper cheek tooth 3)

B   Mandibular duct opening (at rostral end of oral cavity)

Identify and colour:

1   Stylohyoid bone

2   Dorsal buccal salivary glands (in cheek on outer surface of buccinator muscle)

3   Ventral buccal salivary glands (in submucous tissue at lower border of buccinator muscle)

4   Sublingual salivary gland (polystomatic, diffuse part beneath oral mucosa in sublingual fold alongside mandibular duct: opening separately in floor of mouth through about 30 minute papillae)

5   Parotid salivary gland

6   Mandibular salivary gland (seromucous)

7   Parotid salivary duct

8   Mandibular salivary duct

Fig. 51(c) Hyoid Apparatus and Tongue

Label:

A   Apex of tongue

B   Body of tongue

C   Root of tongue

Identify and colour:

1   Stylohyoid bone

2   Occipitohyoid muscle

3   Stylohyoid muscle

4   Thyrohyoid muscle

5   Sternohyoid muscle

6   Ceratohyoid muscle

7   Hyoglossal muscle

8   Mylohyoid muscle

9   Geniohyoid muscle

10   Styloglossal muscle

11   Palatine mucosa (thickened, keratinized and ridged, producing palatine rugae)

12   Mucosa of tongue (filiform and fungiform papillae)

FIGURE 51: THE TONGUE AND SALIVARY GLANDS

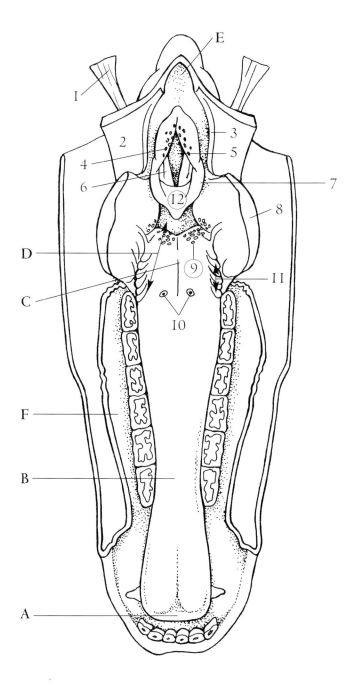

Fig. 51(a) Tongue, palate and larynx – dorsal view

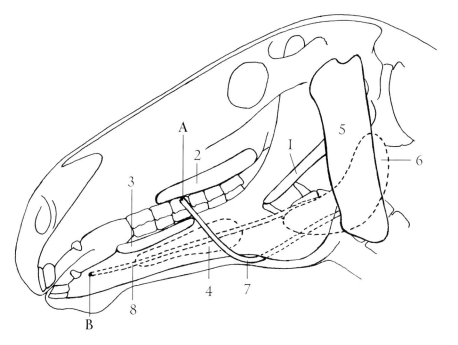

Fig. 51(b) Salivary glands – lateral surface projection

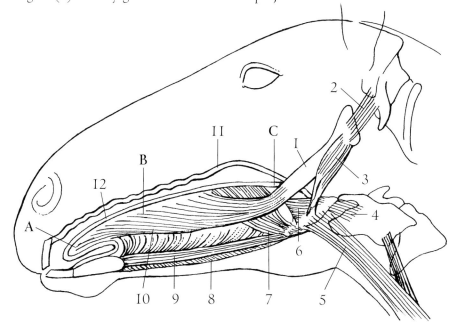

Fig. 51(c) Hyoid apparatus and tongue

IMPLANTATION OF CHEEK TEETH AND MAXILLARY SINUS AT VARIOUS AGES
(Figure 52)

The four drawings show lateral views at ages 2/3, 5, 10 and 20 years. On all appropriate drawings, identify and label:

Deciduous premolars DP1, DP2, DP3

Premolars P2, P3, P4

Molars M1, M2, M3

Identify and colour:

(1)   Rostral maxillary sinus

(2)   Caudal maxillary sinus

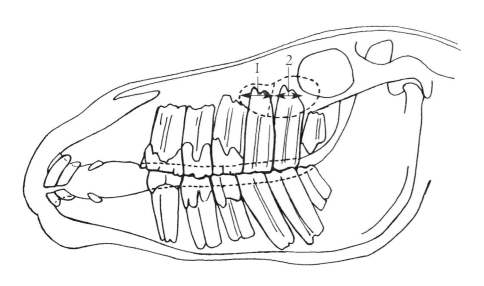

Fig. 52(a) 2/3 years old

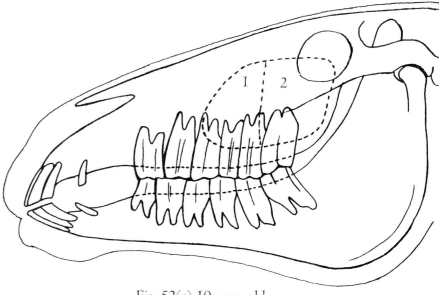

Fig. 52(c) 10 years old

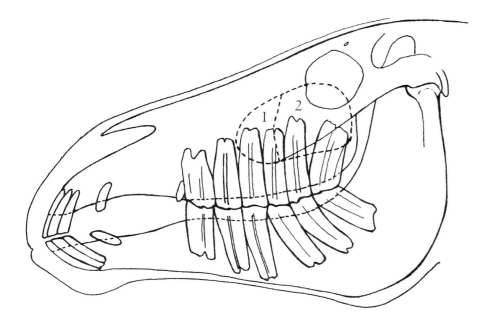

Fig. 52(b) 5 years old

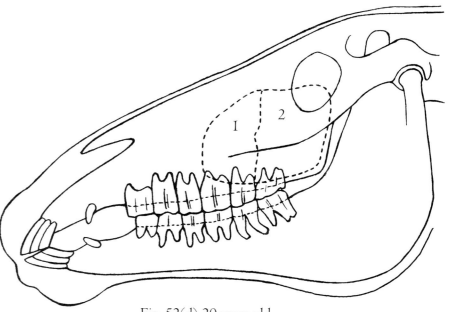

Fig. 52(d) 20 years old

CHEEK TEETH; CENTRAL INCISOR AND ESTIMATION OF AGE – Part I (Figure 53)

Figs. 53(a) and (b) Upper and Lower Dental Arcades – Plan Views

On both drawings, label:

A   Incisor teeth

B   Premolar teeth

C   Molar Teeth

On both drawings, identify and colour:

(I1)   Central incisor tooth

(I2)   Intermediate incisor tooth

(I3)   Corner incisor tooth

(C)   Canine tooth (rudimentary and only erupt in stallions)

(P2)   1st cheek tooth (PI of upper dental arch – wolf tooth – often absent)

(P3)   2nd cheek tooth

(P4)   3rd cheek tooth

(M1)   4th cheek tooth

(M2)   5th cheek tooth

(M3)   6th cheek tooth

Fig. 53(c) Central Incisor – Longitudinal and Transverse Sections

Label:

A   Crown

B   Root

C   Root canal (entry into pulp cavity, constricted as root forms)

Identify and colour:

(1)   Infundibulum ('cup': central depression in tooth table)

(2)   Remains of infundibulum ('mark': central depression occupied initially by central cement and subsequently by central enamel only)

(3)   Peripheral cement (covering entire crown and root: providing attachment for fibres of periodontal membrane holding tooth in socket)

(4)   Central cement (lining infundibulum: continuous with peripheral cement over unworn tooth table)

(5)   Peripheral enamel (hard crystalline surface coating over entire tooth)

(6)   Central enamel (infolded enamel producing infundibulum)

(7)   Dentine (bone-like substance forming bulk of tooth)

(8)   Pulp cavity containing nerves and blood vessels of tooth (dental pulp)

(9)   'Dental star' (secondary dentine deposited in pulp cavity)

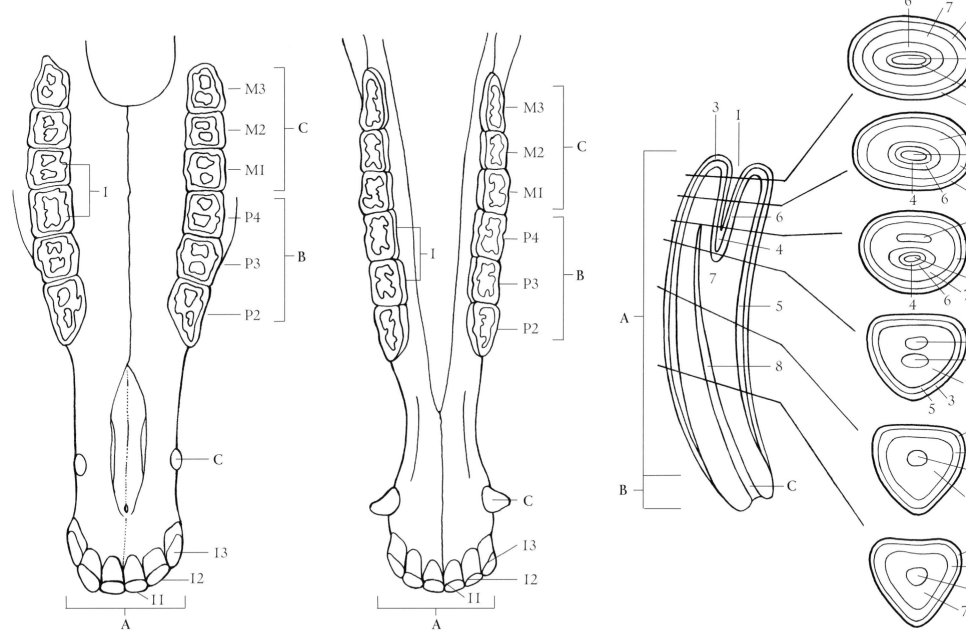

Fig. 53(a) Upper dental arcade – plan view

Fig. 53(b) Lower dental arcade – plan view

Fig. 53(c) Central incisor tooth – longitudinal and transverse sections

INCISOR TEETH AND ESTIMATION OF AGE – Part 2 (Figure 54)

Series of drawings showing incisor teeth of horses of varying ages. Each set of drawings shows, from left to right, (i) incisor teeth from in front, (ii) from the right and (iii) a plan view of the tables of the lower incisors.

Label:

A   Seven-year hook

B   Nine-year hook

C   Galvayne's groove

On each drawing, complete the tooth plan from the front and, referring to Figure 53, identify and colour:

(DI1)   Central temporary (or deciduous) incisor

(DI2)   Intermediate temporary incisor

(DI3)   Corner temporary incisor

(PI1)   Central permanent incisor

(PI2)   Intermediate permanent incisor

(PI3)   Corner temporary incisor

(C)   Canine

(1)   Cup

(2)   Mark

(3)   Dental star

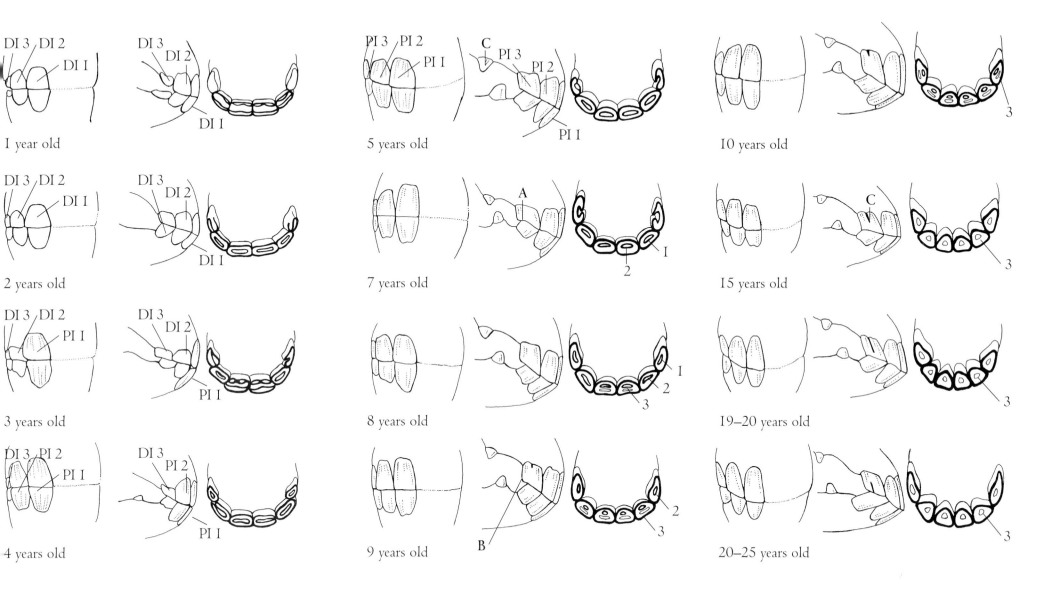

1 year old

2 years old

3 years old

4 years old

5 years old

7 years old

8 years old

9 years old

10 years old

15 years old

19–20 years old

20–25 years old

BLOOD VESSELS IN THE HEAD – Lateral Views
(Figure 55)

Fig. 55(a) Arteries

Identify the following and colour-match the numbered circles with those on the drawing. Colour all the arteries red.

1. Common carotid artery
2. External carotid artery
3. Linguofacial trunk
4. Carotid body (slightly swollen initial part of internal carotid artery containing stretch receptors responsive to changes in blood pressure)
5. Occipital artery
6. Lingual and sublingual arteries
7. Facial artery
8. Buccal artery
9. Mandibular (inferior) alveolar artery
10. Mandibular and maxillary labial arteries
11. Mental artery
12. Dorsal and lateral nasal arteries
13. Angularis oculi artery
14. Infraorbital artery
15. External ethmoidal artery
16. Malar artery
17. External ophthalmic artery
18. Rostral and caudal deep temporal arteries
19. Supraorbital arteries
20. Rostral, lateral and caudal auricular arteries
21. Maxillary artery
22. Superficial temporal artery
23. Internal carotid artery (to brain)
24. Vertebral artery

Fig. 55(b) Veins

Identify the following and colour-match the numbered circles with those on the drawing. Colour all the veins blue.

1. External jugular vein
2. Linguofacial vein
3. Occipital vein
4. Vertebral/occipital vein anastomosis
5. Vertebral vein
6. Superficial temporal vein
7. Rostral, middle and caudal auricular veins
8. Transverse facial vein
9. Maxillary vein
10. Deep temporal veins
11. Supraorbital vein
12. Angular vein of eye
13. Infraorbital vein
14. Sinus of transverse facial vein
15. Sinus of deep facial vein
16. Sinus of buccal vein
17. Masseteric veins
18. Lateral branch of buccal vein
19. Lingual and sublingual veins
20. Deep facial vein
21. Mandibular (inferior) and maxillary (superior) labial veins
22. Mandibular alveolar vein
23. Mental vein
24. Dorsal and lateral nasal veins

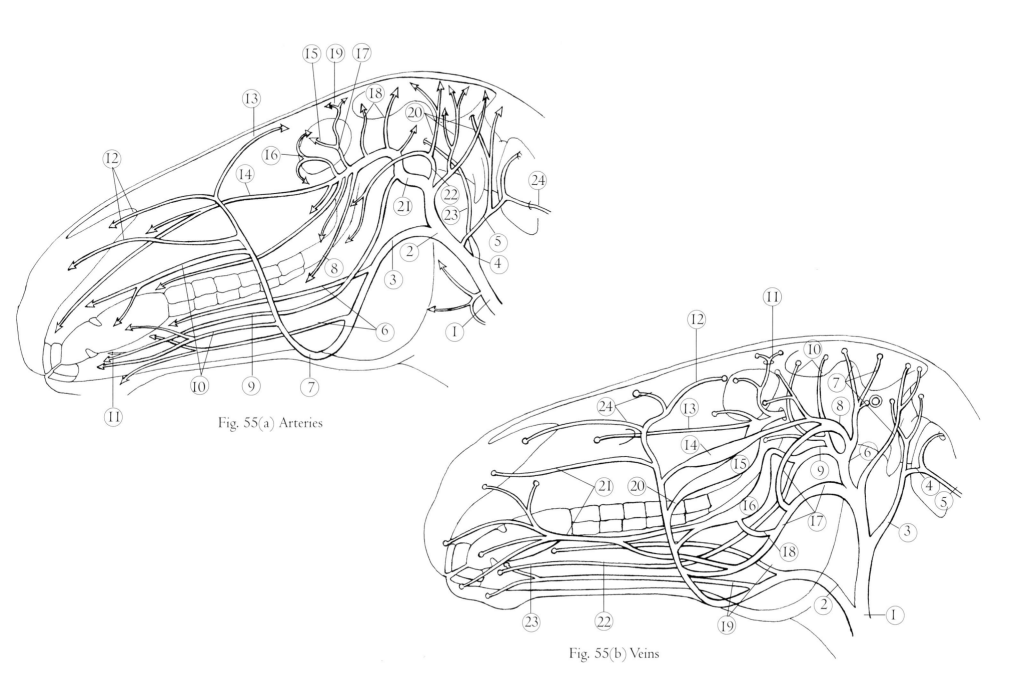

Fig. 55(a) Arteries

Fig. 55(b) Veins

PART 7 – *The Foot*

FIVE VIEWS OF THE FOOT
(Figure 56)

On the drawings on which they occur, label:

A Coronet

B Wall

C Bulbs of the heels

D Collateral groove

E Bar

F Sole

G Frog

H Central groove of frog

I Apex of frog

Identify and colour:

1 Toe

2 Quarter

3 Heel

4 Periople (outer waterproofing layer of hoof wall)

5 White line (layer of pale horn joining wall and sole)

6 Corium of frog (dermis underlying frog, producing tubular and intertubular horn)

7 Coronary corium

8 Laminar corium (dermis on surface of 3rd phalanx underlying wall of hoof and supporting sensitive laminae interleaving with insensitive laminae of wall)

9 Corium of sole (dermis underlying sole, producing tubular and intertubular horn of sole)

10 Perioplic corium (dermis underlying periople)

11 Long pastern bone

12 Short pastern bone

13 Pedal bone

14 Navicular bone

15 Lateral cartilage

FIGURE 56: FIVE VIEWS OF THE FOOT

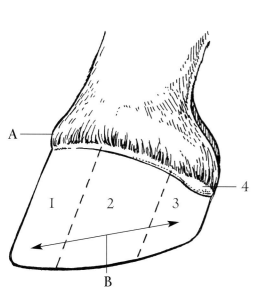

Fig. 56(a) Hoof – lateral view

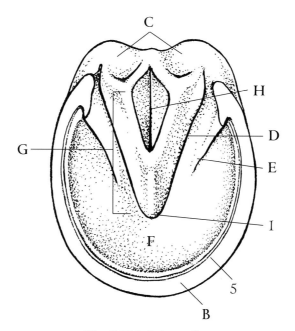

Fig. 56(b) Sole surface

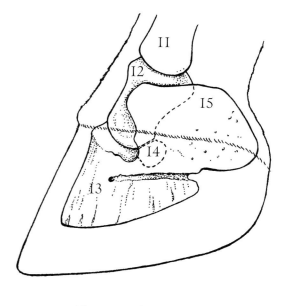

Fig. 56(c) Bones of the foot – lateral view

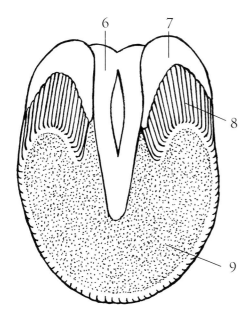

Fig. 56(d) Sole surface of the corium after removal of hoof

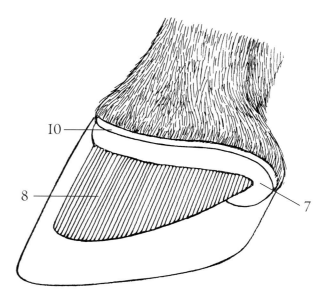

Fig. 56(e) Corium – lateral view

THE FOOT – Vertical, Axial and Transverse Sections
(Figure 57)

(18) Lateral cartilage of 3rd phalanx

(19) White line

On the drawings on which they occur, label:

A   1st phalanx

B   2nd phalanx

C   3rd phalanx

D   Distal sesamoid (navicular) bone

Identify and colour:

(1) Common digital extensor tendon

(2) Perioplic corium

(3) Laminar corium

(4) Corium of frog

(5) Corium of sole

(6) Digital (palmar/plantar) cushion

(7) Distal navicular ligament

(8) Suspensory ligament of navicular bone

(9) Deep digital flexor tendon

(10) Distal sesamoidean ligament

(11) Distal digital annular ligament

(12) Navicular synovial bursa

(13) Synovial cavity of coffin joint

(14) Synovial cavity of pastern joint

(15) Digital synovial tendon sheath

(16) Coffin joint capsule

(17) Periople

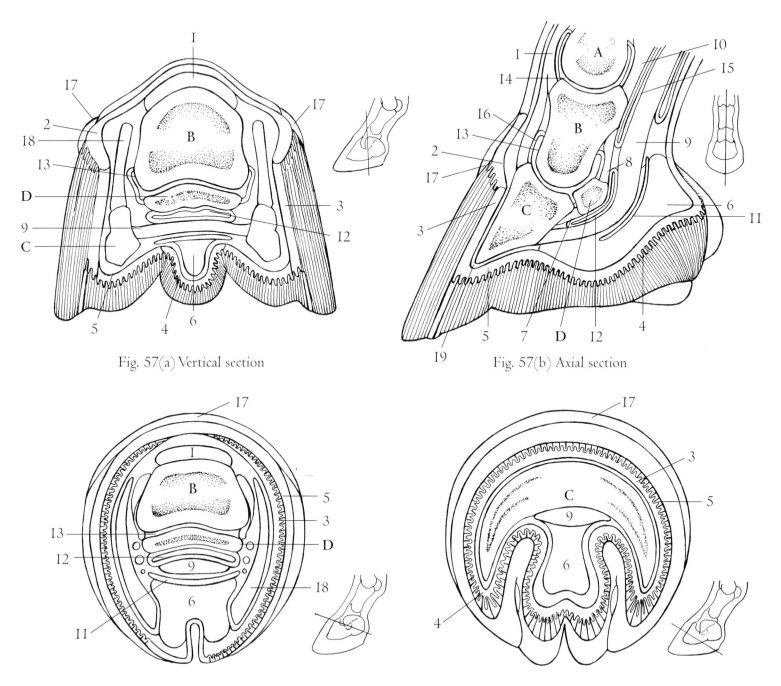

Fig. 57(a) Vertical section

Fig. 57(b) Axial section

Fig. 57(c) Transverse section at level of coronet

Fig. 57(d) Coronet to ground in transverse section

PART 8 — *Viscera*

THE THORAX AND ITS VISCERA (Figure 58)

Figs. 58(a) Thorax in Transverse Section and (b) Lung, Thoracic and Pleural Cavities in Lateral Surface Section

(The small drawing shows the orientation of the main drawings.)

On the two main drawings, as appropriate, label:

A   Thoracic inlet

B   Ist rib

C   18th (last) rib

D   Mediastinum (midline connective tissue partition dividing thoracic cavity into half)

E   Principal bronchus

F   Dorsal border of lung

G   Apical lobe of lung

H   Costal surface of lung

I   Diaphragmatic surface of lung

J   Ventral border of lung

K   Visceral pericardium (epicardium on surface of heart)

L   Parietal pericardium

Identify and colour:

1. Supraspinous ligament
2. Thoracic vertebra and longus thoracis muscles (roof of thoracic cavity)
3. Ribs and intercostal muscles (wall of thoracic cavity)
4. Lungs
5. Thoracic aorta
6. Azygos vein
7. Oesophagus
8. Tracheal bifurcation
9. Heart in pericardium
10. Sternum and transverse thoracic muscles (floor of thoracic cavity)
11. Connective tissue of mediastinum
12. Contour of diaphragam

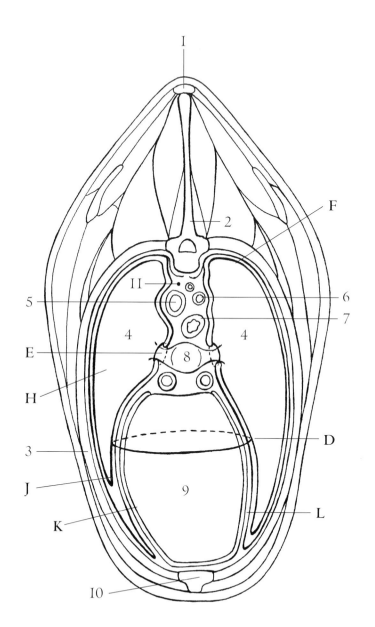

Fig. 58(a) Thorax in transverse section

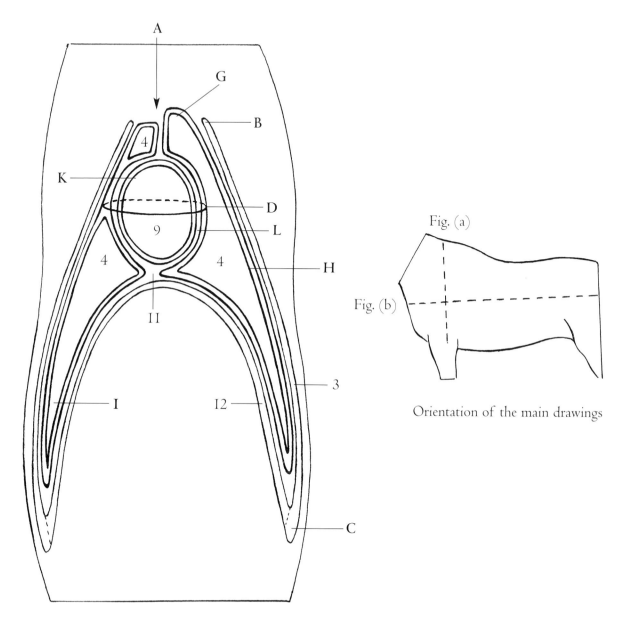

Fig. 58(b) Lung, thoracic and pleural cavities in
lateral surface section

Orientation of the main drawings

ABDOMINAL AND PELVIC VISCERA (Figure 59)

Figs. 59(a) Abdomen in Transverse Section and (b) Abdomen and Pelvis in Frontal Section

(The small drawing shows the orientation of the main drawings.)

On the two main drawings, as appropriate, label:

A   Visceral peritoneum

B   Parietal peritoneum of abdomen

C   Abdominal wall and floor

D   Caudal boundary of abdominal cavity

E   Parietal peritoneum of pelvis

Identify and colour:

1   Abdominal roof (lumbar vertebrae and sublumbar muscles)

2   Descending duodenum

3   Base of caecum

4   Right ventral colon

5   Caudal vena cava

6   Abdominal aorta

7   Left kidney

8   Small (descending) colon

9   Left dorsal colon

10   Left ventral colon

11   Coils of small intestine (mainly jejunum)

12   Body of caecum

13   Caecocolic ligament

14   Intercolic ligament connecting left dorsal and left ventral colon

15   Intercolic ligament connecting right dorsal and right ventral colon

16   Great mesentery

17   Linea alba

18   Liver

19   Stomach

20   Retroperitoneal component of pelvic cavity

21   Spleen

22   Right dorsal colon

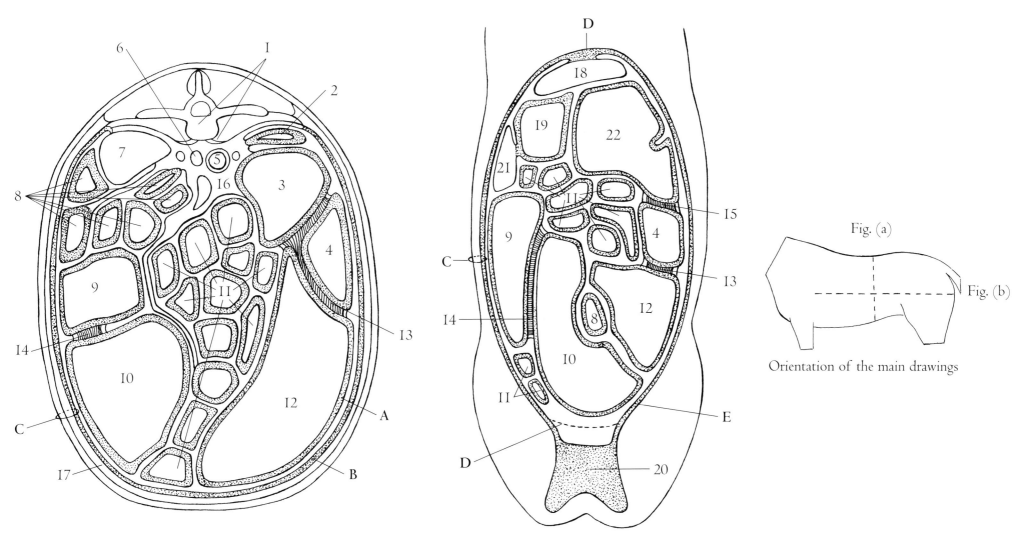

Fig. 59(a) Abdomen in transverse section

Fig. 59(b) Abdomen and pelvis in frontal section

Orientation of the main drawings

GUT SCHEMA – Left
Lateral View (Figure 60)

Label:

A   Anal canal

B   Stomach

C   Dorsal diaphragmatic flexure of colon

D   Ventral diaphragmatic (sternal) flexure of colon

E   Pelvic flexure

F   Great mesentery

Identify and colour:

(1)   Rectum

(2)   Small colon (descending colon)

(3)   Transverse colon

(4)   Descending duodenum

(5)   Right dorsal colon

(6)   Caecum

(7)   Right ventral colon

(8)   Ileum

(9)   Caecocolic ligament

(10)   Intercolic ligament connecting right dorsal and
       right ventral colon

(11)   Intercolic ligament connecting left ventral and left
       dorsal colon

(12)   Left dorsal colon

(13)   Left ventral colon

(14)   Lateral free band of left ventral colon

(15)   Coils of small intestine (mainly jejunum)

(16)   Cranial mesenteric artery

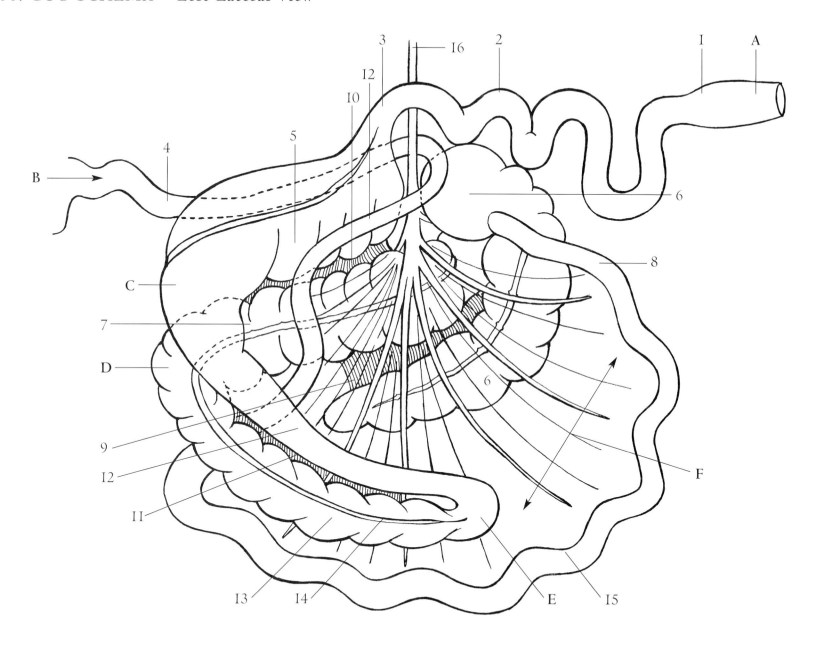

THORACIC, ABDOMINAL AND PELVIC VISCERA OF THE MARE – Lateral Superficial View (Figure 61)

Identify and colour:

1. Oesophagus
2. Trachea
3. Left lung
4. Heart
5. Ventral diaphragmatic flexure of colon
6. Left ventral colon
7. Small intestine (jejunum)
8. Small colon or descending colon
9. Left kidney
10. Ventral sacrococcygeal muscle
11. Rectum (intrapelvic part of small colon)
12. Coccygeal muscle
13. Levator ani muscle
14. Constrictor vulvae muscle
15. External anal sphincter muscle
16. Anus
17. Vulva
18. Costal muscle fibres of diaphragm

FIGURE 61: THORACIC, ABDOMINAL AND PELVIC VISCERA OF THE MARE –
Lateral Superficial View

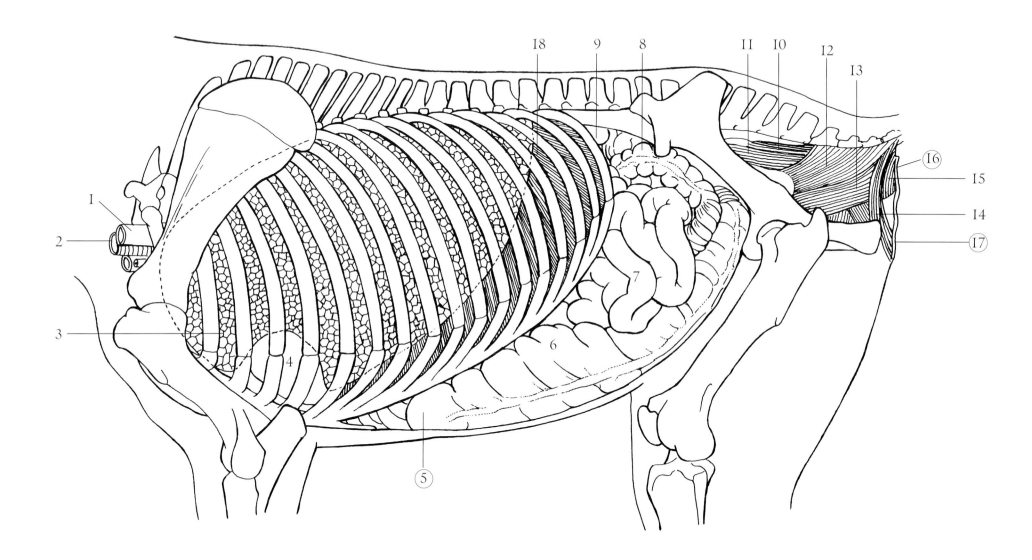

THORACIC, ABDOMINAL AND PELVIC VISCERA OF THE MARE – Lateral Deep View
(Figure 62)

Identify and colour:

1. Oesophagus
2. Trachea
3. Cranial vena cava
4. Thoracic lymphatic duct
5. Aorta
6. Pulmonary trunk
7. Left bronchus
8. Right ventricle
9. Left ventricle
10. Coronary artery and vein
11. Left atrium
12. Liver
13. Stomach
14. Spleen
15. Diaphragm
16. Left kidney
17. Small colon (descending colon)
18. Small intestine (jejunum)
19. Left dorsal colon
20. Dorsal diaphragmatic flexure of colon
21. Ventral diaphragmatic flexure of colon
22. Left ventral colon
23. Lateral free band of left ventral colon
24. Left uterine horn
25. Left ovary
26. Left fallopian tube
27. Body of uterus
28. Cervix (neck of uterus)
29. Left ureter
30. Urinary bladder
31. Urethra surrounded by the urethralis muscle
32. Rectum
33. Anus
34. Vulva
35. Mammary gland (udder)
36. Teat

FIGURE 62: THORACIC, ABDOMINAL AND PELVIC VISCERA OF THE MARE –
Lateral Deep View

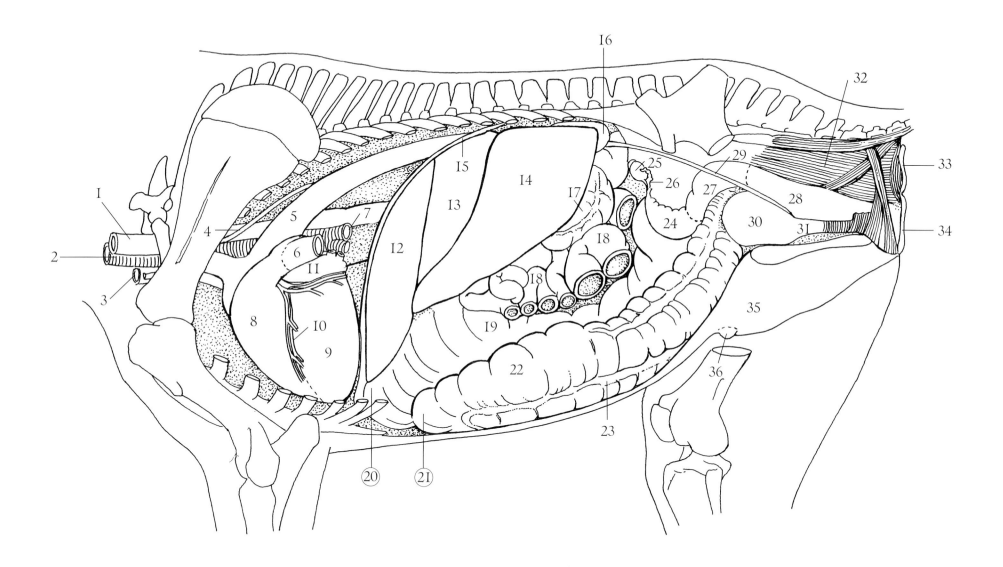

THORACIC, ABDOMINAL AND PELVIC VISCERA OF THE STALLION – Lateral Superficial View (Figure 63)

Indentify and colour:

(1) Right lung

(2) Heart

(3) Ventral diaphragmatic flexure of colon

(4) Lateral free band of right ventral colon

(5) Right ventral colon

(6) Base of caecum

(7) Duodenum

(8) Body of caecum

(9) Lateral caecal band

(10) Apex of caecum

(11) Right ureter

(12) Vas deferens

(13) Pelvic flexure of colon

(14) Urinary bladder

(15) Seminal vesicle

(16) Prostate gland

(17) Bulbourethral gland

(18) Ischiocavernosus muscle

(19) Root of penis

(20) Gracilis muscle

(21) Body of penis

(22) Right testicle, or testis

(23) Epididymis

(24) Scrotum

(25) External fold of prepuce

(26) Spermatic cord

(27) Prepuce (sheath)

(28) Glans penis

(29) Bulbospongiosus muscle

(30) Retractor penis muscle

(31) Rectum

(32) Small intestine

(33) Costal muscle fibres of diaphragm

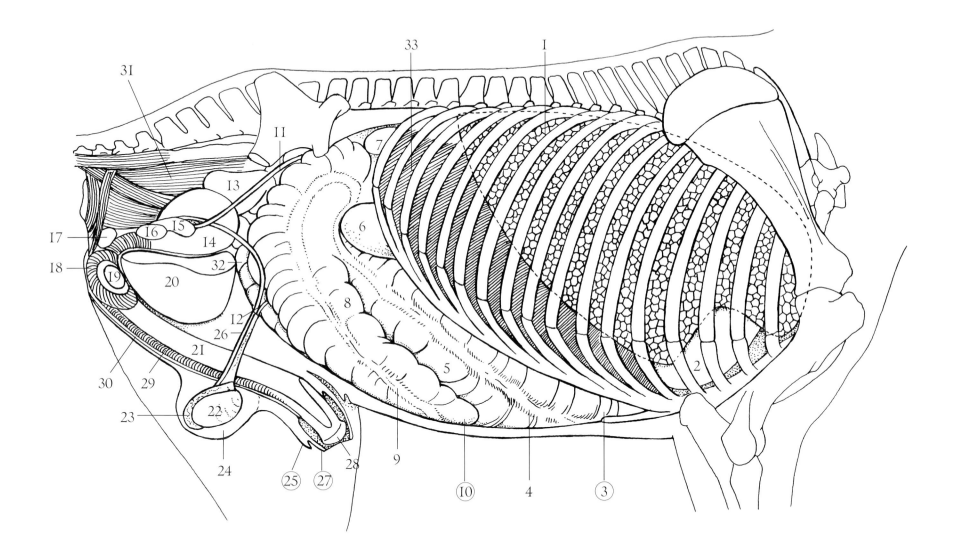

THORACIC, ABDOMINAL AND PELVIC VISCERA OF THE STALLION – Lateral Deep View
(Figure 64)

Identify and colour:

1. Trachea
2. Oesophagus
3. Right bronchus
4. Cranial vena cava
5. Right atrium
6. Caudal vena cava
7. Left ventricle
8. Right ventricle
9. Coronary artery and vein
10. Azygos vein
11. Aorta
12. Diaphragm
13. Right lobe of liver
14. Dorsal sac of caecum
15. Descending duodenum
16. Right kidney
17. Body of caecum
18. Lateral caecal band
19. Right dorsal colon
20. Right ventral colon
21. Lateral free band of right ventral colon
22. Ventral diaphragmatic flexure of colon
23. Diaphragmatic flexure of right dorsal colon
24. Pelvic flexure of colon
25. Urinary bladder
26. Pelvic part of urethra
27. Bulb of penis
28. Spongy body of penis
29. Penile urethra
30. Cavernous body of penis
31. Glans penis
32. External urethral orifice
33. Anus

FIGURE 64: THORACIC, ABDOMINAL AND PELVIC VISCERA OF THE STALLION –
Lateral Deep View

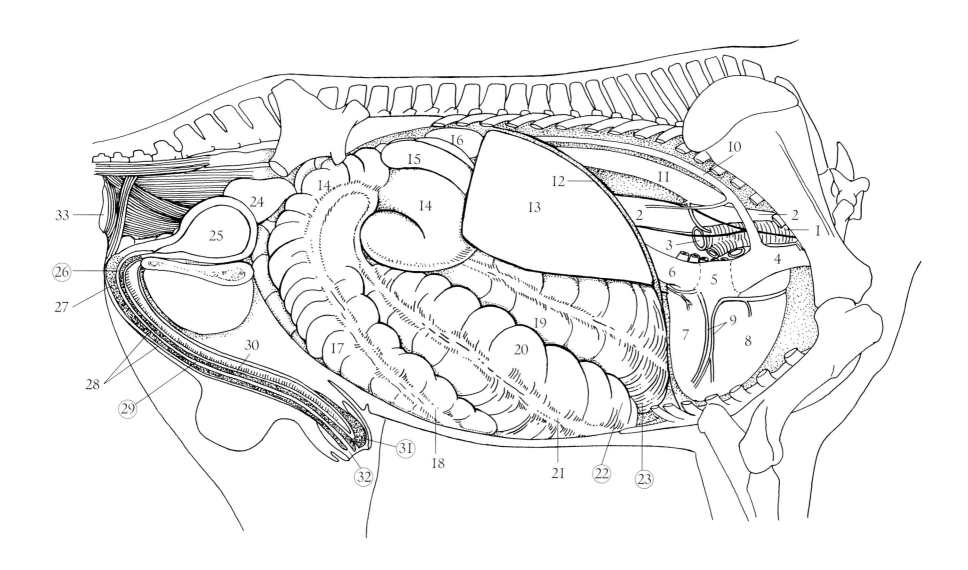

About the Author

Maggie Raynor is a highly regarded professional illustrator who studied fine art at Sheffield College of Art and the Royal College of Art. Her anatomical drawings have appeared in a number of books on human and equine medicine. She has also provided the artwork for many well-known books on training horses; her own equestrian skills and powers of observation helping to convey the precise detail required. She is the joint author of *Basic Schooling Made Simple* and the humorous work *Equitation – The Truth* and provided all the illustrations for both titles.